Personal Training & Workout DIARY

Published by Hinkler Books Pty Ltd
45–55 Fairchild Street
Heatherton Victoria 3202 Australia
www.hinkler.com

Cover design: Hinkler Design Studio
Illustrator: Hector Aiza/3DLabz

ISBN: 978 1 4889 1440 9

Printed and bound in China

Image credits:
Images © Shutterstock.com: Active bicyclist © Kalmatsuy Tatyana; Man and woman on a elliptical cross trainer © Holbox; Fresh fruit salad © ElenaGaak.

It is recommended that you check with your doctor or healthcare professional before commencing any exercise regime. While every care has been taken in the preparation of this material, the publishers and their respective employees or agents will not accept responsibility for injury or damage occasioned to any person as a result of participation in the activities described in this book.

INTRODUCTION

How often have you said, "I need to exercise," but not followed through? Have you started an exercise program only to stop within weeks? When starting a training program, most people's intentions aren't to stop after a short while. Unfortunately, this is often exactly what happens. It would be great to be fit and healthy with no effort, but it can take a lot of hard work to achieve your fitness and weight loss goals.

A personal training diary can help you reach those goals. Recording training sessions and food intake makes you more aware of what you put in your body and how you burn it off. This information can help you set goals and targets, plan exercise sessions, and learn what works for you.

Health, Fitness, and Weight

While most people would like to keep slim and fit, there are also serious reasons for maintaining a healthy weight. The World Health Organization (WHO) estimates that at least one in three adults are overweight and one in 10 are obese. Even a slightly overweight person has a higher risk of health problems, which increases the more overweight a person is. Improving fitness and maintaining a healthy weight has many benefits, including:

- a reduction in the risk of heart disease, stroke, diabetes, osteoarthritis, cancer, skin problems, respiratory conditions, infertility, gallbladder disease, and hypertension
- increased lean muscle, body tone, strength, endurance, cardiovascular fitness, and energy levels
- increased core and joint stability, reducing related pain and injuries
- better recovery from injury and illness
- posture and flexibility improvements
- improved performance levels, greater self-confidence, and better sleep patterns
- a stronger metabolism, increasing the rate the body burns fat.

While excess weight can cause health problems, it's also something that you can control. While your genes can influence weight, the most effective way to become lean is through a combination of strength and cardiovascular training. The other vital ingredient is a sensible, healthy eating plan.

Remember, if you are starting a new diet or exercise regime, have a check-up with your doctor first. By making changes to your diet and lifestyle, you'll reduce your risk of disease, feel happier, have more energy, sleep better, handle stress more effectively, and look great!

Calculating BMI

The body mass index (BMI) measures whether someone is considered overweight. To obtain your BMI, use the following formula:

BMI = weight in pounds divided by the square of height in inches, then multiplied by 703

A woman who weighs 167lb (76kg) and is 70in (1.79m) tall works out her BMI by dividing 167 by 4900 (her height of 70 squared, or 70 x 70). 167 divided by 4900 equals 0.3408. This amount, multiplied by 703, equals a BMI of 23.95.

The classifications used by the WHO are :

Classification	BMI
Underweight	< 18.50
Healthy range	18.50–24.99
Overweight	25.00–29.99
Obese	30.00–39.99
Morbidly obese	> 40.00

Body shape, build and ethnic origin affect BMI, so it is a guide only. People from an Asian background are classified as overweight if their BMI is more than 23 and people from a Pacific Islander background are classified as overweight if their BMI is more than 26. Do not use the BMI for children under 15, or the elderly.

The risks are greater if a person has excess fat around the abdomen. If your BMI is over 25 and your waist measures more than 37in (94cm) for men and 31.5in (80cm) for women, the risk of disease is greater than for a person who gains weight on other parts of their body, such as their hips and thighs.

Checking your waist–hip ratio can be a good way to assess your risk of heart disease, diabetes, and some cancers. Measure your weight at its narrowest point and your hips at their widest. Divide your waist measurement by your hip measurement to get your ratio. Ideally, women should have a waist–hip ratio of 0.85 or less and men should have a waist–hip ratio of 0.9 or less.

Strength Training

Strength or resistance training improves muscle and bone density, metabolic rate, muscle mass, and endurance. This is important as you age, as older people's muscles lose strength. Strength or resistance training includes free weights, training machines, exercising with bands or tubes, and calisthenics (such as sit-ups, push-ups, and pull-ups).

The WHO recommends at least two or three sessions a week of resistance or weight training. Each session should be at least 20 minutes long. The intensity and weight will vary depending on your strength and fitness levels. Have at least a day's break between sessions for muscles to recover.

Technique and Breathing

Technique is important to reduce the risk of injury and get the most from a workout. Start at an easy level and ensure you have mastered the technique before progressing. A single repeat of a movement is a repetition and a group of repetitions is a set. Breathe as normally as possible. Exhale on the exertion part of the movement and inhale on the return movement. Generally allow around two minutes recovery time between sets of the same exercise or exercises of the same muscle group.

Load

Load is the resistance applied to each repetition. Increasing the weight, slowing a movement, or changing position can increase a movement's load and intensity.

Training Intensity

To increase strength, a gradual and progressive increase in workload is required. After a load increase, gradually increase repetitions to the set target and then increase the load again. To ensure your body is getting the best possible workout, take your muscles to a point they haven't previously been. This may mean working to muscle failure.

Cardio Training

Cardiovascular training conditions the heart and lungs. It contributes to heart health, oxygen uptake and use, endurance, energy, and fitness. Cardio training affects metabolism and the body's use of fat as an energy source.

Frequency

The WHO recommends at least 150 minutes of moderate activity or 75 minutes of vigorous activity a week. For extra benefit, increase moderate activity to 300 minutes or vigorous activity to 150 minutes a week. If you currently do no cardio training, a few times a week is appropriate to begin. Don't believe "more training is better." If you over-train, you won't achieve faster: you can end up sore, tired, frustrated, injured, and back where you started.

Length of Cardio Sessions

The length of each session depends on your fitness level and the intensity level that you exercise at. The more intense a session, the shorter it can be. Below is a list of cardiovascular activities and their recommended duration.

Activity	Duration
Walking	30–60 minutes
Jogging/running	15–40 minutes
Cycling	20–60 minutes
Swimming	20–40 minutes
Skipping	15–30 minutes
Stair walking or running	15–30 minutes
Aerobics or water aerobics class	45–60 minutes
Tennis, squash, golf, touch rugby, bowls, cricket, football, netball, basketball, softball, baseball, soccer	30–60 minutes
Boxing, martial arts, boxercise	30–60 minutes

Intensity of Cardio Sessions

Exercise at a level that enables your muscles to respond and adapt. If your level is too easy, you will only maintain your fitness level. However, don't push yourself too hard. Cardio exercise should make you breathe heavily and your heart beat faster. If you can talk between heavy breathing, then your intensity is appropriate.

Start at an easy-to-moderate intensity and gradually increase it. Moderate exercise includes brisk walking, light weight training, cycling, and mowing the lawn. Increase cardiovascular intensity by going faster or longer or making the exercise more difficult.

Also try to have a few sessions of more vigorous exercise of least 30 minutes. This should make you sweat and puff so that talking is very hard. It includes jogging, fast swimming, exercise classes, squash, singles tennis, power walking, team sports, and fast cycling.

Activity	Approx. cal/kJ burned per hour	Activity	Approx. cal/kJ burned per hour
Sleeping	55/230	Basketball	420/1750
Eating	85/355	Aerobics	450/1885
Sitting	85/355	Moderate cycling	450/1885
Standing	100/420	Jogging	500/2090
Driving	110/460	Digging	500/2090
Housework	160/670	Fast swimming	500/2090
Golf	240/1000	Cross trainer	500/2090
Calisthenics	240/1000	Hiking	500/2090
Slow cycling	240/1000	Step class	550/2300
Slow walking	240/1000	Rowing	550/2300
Gardening	250/1045	Power walking	600/2510
Walking	280/1170	Heavy weight training	600/2510
Slow swimming	300/1250	Boxing (sparring)	630/2640
Tennis (singles)	350/1465	Exercise bike or fast cycling	650/2720
Yoga	400/1675		
Rollerblading	420/1750	Squash	650/2720
Vigorous dancing	420/1750	Skipping	700/2390
Brisk walking	420/1750	Running	700/2390

Stretching and Flexibility

Stretching is an important part of exercise programs, yet it's often neglected. This can jeopardize a program's long-term effectiveness. Stretching two or three times a week makes your exercise more effective and your body more supple.

Regular stretching keeps you flexible and helps prevent muscle injury and soreness. It improves muscle elasticity by increasing blood flow to the muscles and helps lengthen and strengthen them. Never hold your breath as you stretch. Perform a range of long, slow stretches that target different muscles one by one.

The best time to stretch is after training, as the muscles are already warm and more pliable and can be moved into positions where a long-term benefit can result. Each stretch needs to be performed correctly: technique is a priority to ensure full effect and to prevent injuries. Try the following stretches after a workout. Hold each stretch for 30–60 seconds.

Triceps Stretch

Stand up straight. Lift both arms above your head and bend your elbows. Hold your right elbow with your left hand and push it down behind your back and hold. Repeat with the other arm.

Shoulder Stretch

Place your left arm across your body, keeping it parallel to the ground. With your other hand, push in toward your chest and hold. Repeat with the other arm.

Lower-back Stretch

Lie on your back. Pull one knee up to your chest until you feel a stretch. Hold your knee to your chest with your arms. Make sure the other leg remains flat on the ground. Hold and then repeat with the other leg.

Hip Flexor Stretch

Keeping your back straight, kneel forward on one knee. Place the other foot in front, keeping your bottom tucked under. Lean forward so that your weight is on the front leg. Hold and then repeat with the other leg.

Standing Quadriceps Stretch

Stand straight, using an object for support if necessary. Hold your ankle and pull your foot up behind until you feel a stretch. Hold and then repeat with the other leg.

Standing Adductor Stretch

Standing with feet apart, lunge sideways to the left, bending your knee and taking your weight on your left leg until you feel a stretch in your groin. Hold and then repeat on the other side.

Upper Back Stretch

Kneel on your hands and knees. Stretch your arms out in front as your head drops down toward the floor and your bottom moves back toward your heels until you feel a stretch. Hold.

Torso Twist Stretch

Sit on the floor with your right leg stretched out in front. Bend your left leg over your right knee. Place your left arm behind you for support and your right arm outside your left knee. Rotate your left shoulder and hold. Repeat on the other side.

Seated Adductor

Sit on the floor with your knees bent and the soles of your feet together in front of you. As you relax your knees to the floor, pull your heels toward you until you feel a stretch in your groin. Hold.

Abdominal and Lower Back Stretch

Lie face-down on the floor with your hands out in front, supporting your body weight. Straighten your elbows to raise your chest until you feel a stretch in your lower back and abdomen. Hold. If this is difficult, hold your arms further out in front.

Calf Stretch

If necessary, lean against a wall or an object for support. Place your right foot in front of you with your knee bent and your left leg straight out behind. Keeping your left heel on the ground, lean forward until you feel a stretch. Hold, then repeat with the other leg.

Lumbar Rotation Stretch

Lie on your back with your legs together. Pull both legs up to your chest and then rotate them to one side, keeping your shoulders flat on the floor. Hold and then repeat on the other side.

Warming Up and Cooling Down

Warming up before exercise involves slowly building up activity so that blood flow to the muscles increases and warms the tissues, the heart rate slowly increases, and adrenalin is released to lubricate the joints. A warm-up should relate to the exercise that you're about to do. If you are going to exercise your legs, do some gentle jogging on the spot. Some easy stretches should also be performed. For strength training, perform one or two easy warm-up sets before commencing.

Cooling down can help delay and reduce muscle soreness and is done at a lower intensity than the exercise. It keeps the blood flowing through the muscles and prevents dizziness and the build up of lactic acid. Slowly reduce the rate of exercise for five to ten minutes and perform a series of stretches.

Setting Goals and Staying Motivated

Achieving empowers and motivates you to keep improving. Goals should be realistic, challenging, specific, and measureable, with a time frame and a plan for their completion. If necessary, talk to a fitness professional about what targets are appropriate.

Set challenging but achievable short, medium, and long-term goals, as you'll lose motivation if you fail to reach your targets. For example, a short-term goal is to walk 3mi (5km) in under 40 minutes in a month. A medium-term goal is to run 1.8mi (3km) without stopping in three months. A long-term goal is to compete in a 5mi (8km) fun run in six months.

Competing against yourself is a great way to get results. Try to beat your previous time or perform more repetitions. Look for handy gadgets such as pedometers, heart-rate monitors, and distance monitors to measure your performance.

It is easy to lose motivation if you try to achieve too much, or if you do activities that you don't enjoy or that don't fit your lifestyle. Choose a variety of activities so you won't get bored or frustrated. Exercising with a friend or a trainer is a great way to keep motivated. There's no better motivation than reaching your goals and seeing the results!

Exercise and Activity Tips

- Be active every day. Look for ways to be active in your daily life and make exercise a regular part of your family and social life.
- Regard exercise as a bonus, not a bother. Choose activities that you enjoy.
- Join a gym or fitness club, get a personal trainer, or play a team sport
- Work out with an exercise partner
- Set goals and try to beat them. Don't be unrealistic with your targets.
- Train for an event or competition
- Use a training journal.

Nutrition

The main reason for eating is to provide the body with the energy it needs day to day. Many people skip meals or make bad choices when they need quality nutrition and energy. The problem gets worse when people eat the majority of their food in the evening, when they least need it.

A Healthy Diet

A good diet is made up of foods that are high in fiber and low in fat. A healthy diet focuses on a variety of foods that provide the body with the right amount of fuel and nutrition. Read the labels on food packaging to see what nutrients, fat content, and energy the food contains. An up-to-date fat, fiber, kilojoule/calorie counter is a great help.

Everyone's nutritional needs vary, but below are some general daily guidelines.

Daily, women should aim to eat:

- 4–7 serves of vegetables
- 4–6 serves of wholegrain cereal, bread, rice, pasta, and noodles
- 2–3 serves of fruit
- 2–3 serves of low-fat milk, yogurt, cheese, and other dairy foods
- 1–1½ serves of eggs, legumes, and nuts
- 0–2½ serves of "extra" foods (high in fat, sugar, or salt)
- 3 pints (1.5L) of fluid.

Daily, men should aim to eat:

- 6–8 serves of vegetables
- 5–7 serves of wholegrain cereal, bread, rice, pasta, and noodles
- 3–4 serves of fruit
- 2–4 serves of low-fat milk, yogurt, cheese, and other dairy foods
- 1–1½ serves of eggs, legumes, and nuts
- 0–3 serves of "extra" foods (high in fat, sugar, or salt)
- 3 pints (1.5L) of fluid.

Try to eat lean meat and poultry only two or three times a week and fish at least once or twice a week. Drink plenty of water and fluids to avoid dehydration.

To maintain a healthy diet, avoid:

- Fat, especially saturated fats
- Sugar and sugary food and drinks
- Fatty cuts of meat and processed meats
- Salt
- Alcohol (limit to one per day for women and two per day for men).

Drink coffee, tea, and fruit juice in moderation, as coffee and tea contain caffeine and juice contains kilojoules/calories.

Healthy Dieting Tips

- Reduce portion sizes. However, increase the number of red, green, and yellow vegetable servings. Try adding an extra vegetable to your meals.
- Eat smaller meals more regularly
- Plan your meals ahead of time. Prepare healthy snacks, such as fruit, nuts, or wholemeal crackers.
- Read the labels on food products. Some "low fat" foods are high in sugar or kilojoules/calories.
- Don't boil vegetables for too long, as they lose their nutrients and flavor
- Use herbs and spices to flavor food instead of fatty sauces or salt
- Choose wholegrain cereals over white or processed cereals
- Eat lots of fiber to feel fuller. Always eat a high-fiber breakfast, such as bran, whole wheat or oat cereal.
- Don't set unachievable weight-loss goals.

Diet, Exercise, Supplements, and Vitamins

A well-planned, healthy diet that meets all nutritional needs is important for sporting and athletic performance. Consult a doctor or a sports nutritionist for the best ways to combine exercise, training, and diet for optimum performance and results.

Carbohydrates are the most effective source of energy, as they are broken down into glucose, which is used as an energy source by the muscles when you exercise. Nutritionists recommend that over half of energy intake should come from carbohydrates. Athletes and strength trainers may need to increase that amount to two thirds of their energy intake. No more than a third of energy should come from fats and about 15 percent from proteins.

Protein and amino acid supplements are popular with athletes and strength trainers. While athletes do require more protein in their diet, health professionals recommend this comes from a healthy diet. The recommended daily amount of protein for a regular, active person is 0.03oz (0.75g) of protein per 2.2lb (1kg) of body weight. For sportspeople, that can increase from 0.03oz (0.75g) to 0.04oz (1kg) per 2.2lb (1kg) and for high performance endurance athletes and strength trainers, that amount can increase to up to 0.06oz (1.7g) of protein per 2.2lb (1kg).

Significantly higher protein intake can be harmful. Excess consumption of protein can lead to dehydration, kidney failure, reduced bone density, and weight gain. Drink lots of water if you are on a high-protein diet and only take protein supplements (such as whey protein), bars and shakes if you are not getting enough protein in your daily diet.

A small amount of protein (such as a yogurt or a bowl of cereal) before and after you exercise can increase muscle development. After your workout, try to eat foods that combine protein and carbohydrates to optimize how muscles rebuild and repair. Avoid sugary foods and drinks.

A healthy diet should also contain an adequate amount of vitamins and minerals. Use vitamin supplements as directed and do not take higher than recommended doses, as some vitamins and minerals are toxic in larger amounts.

How to Use the Diary

This diary is designed as a complete record of your exercise sessions and results over twelve months. It is divided into days, weeks, months, and a year so you can monitor exercise and dietary practices and behaviors. As the diary is not dated, you can start recording information at any time.

Twelve-month Planner

The diary starts off with a twelve-month planner that allows you to record events over the course of a year. Use this section to fill in major events and occurrences that could affect your exercise sessions and dietary habits throughout the year.

Yearly Assessments

Record your details at the start and end of the twelve-month period covered by the diary. Use the first assessment page at the beginning of your program to set out your measurements and targets. The end-of-year assessment lets you assess whether you've met or surpassed those goals.

Weekly Records

The weekly record forms the major part of the diary. Set weekly targets, plan your calorie intake, and record your weight, BMI, and waist–hip ratio. There's also space to record lifestyle information.

The exercise diary lets you enter your strength and cardio training sessions throughout the week. Record the focus area, the equipment used, the number of sets and reps, and the weight you've used in your strength training. Use the cardio training page to note information such as heart rate, exercise intensity, and calories burnt.

Use the food diary to record your daily totals of fat and calories. Add up the totals to show your overall weekly food consumption and compare it against your goal from the start of the week.

Monthly Evaluation

Use the monthly evaluation pages to set goals and measure your progress over the past month. Check your average daily calorie and fat consumption over the course of a month. By assessing your weight, fitness, and body measurements at the start of the month and comparing it against your results at the end of the month, you'll not only have a great idea of your progress but also be motivated to keep up the good work!

Yearly Heart-rate Graph

The heart-rate graph is a great visual way to track your fitness over the course of twelve months. Each week, simply mark your resting and maximum heart rates on the graph. As the year progresses, you'll get a good idea of how you are doing with your program.

Personal Bests

Record your best times and results in this section. Update the chart with your progress and new bests, and use this information to help set new goals and targets.

The Muscular System

The human body contains more than 600 muscles. Each muscle performs a particular function, and they all work together to operate the human body.

The Muscular System: Male

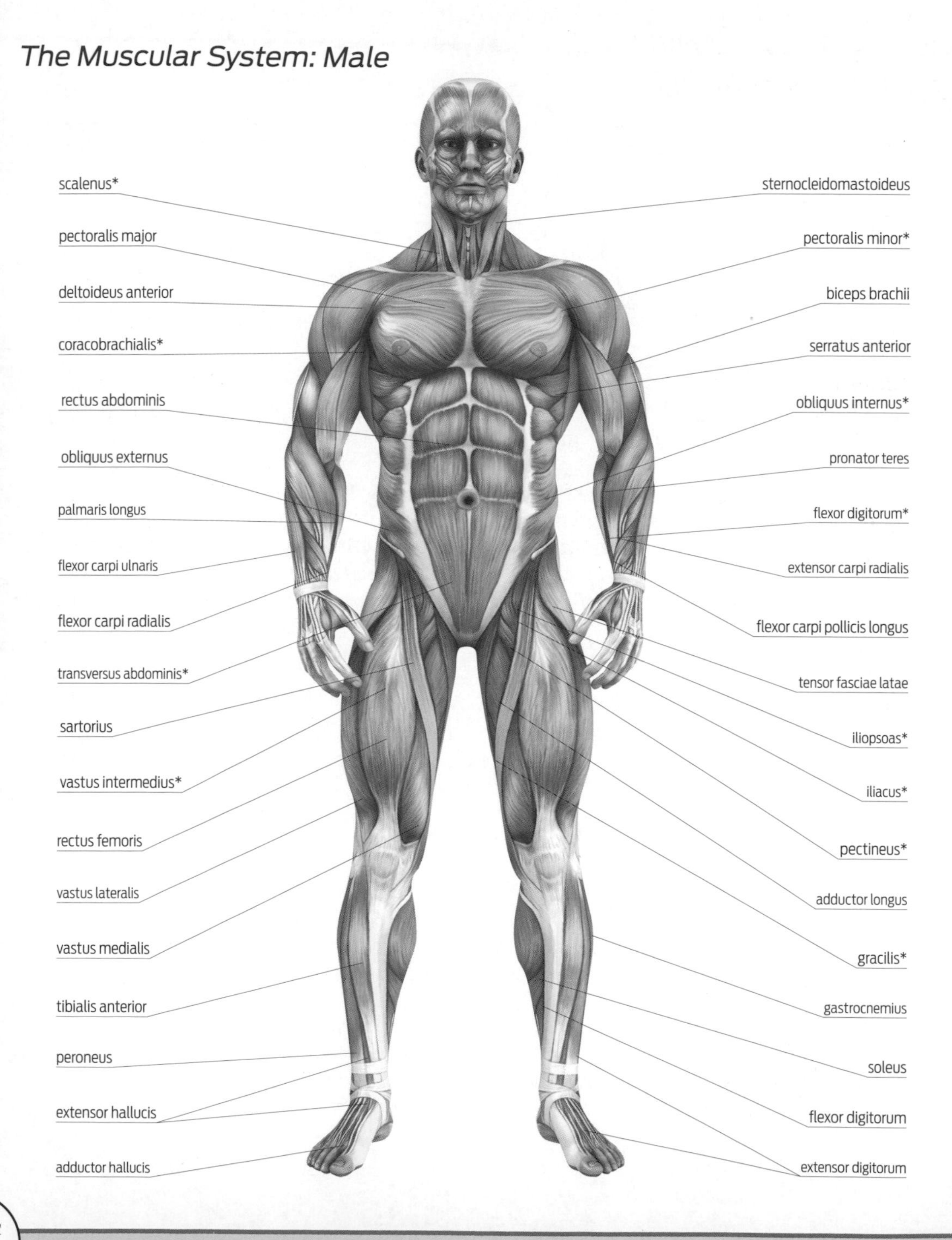

Annotation Key
* Indicates deep muscles

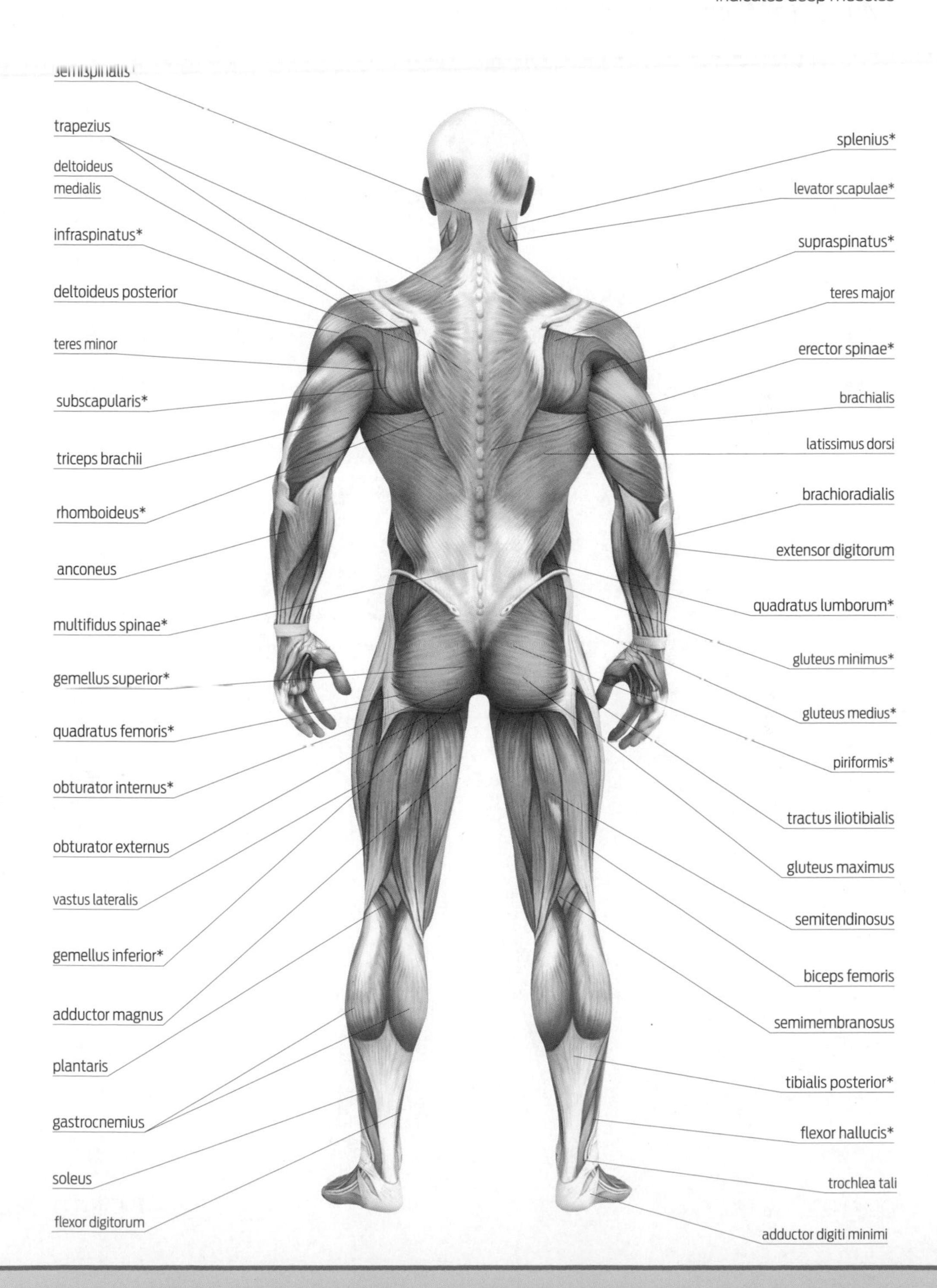

The Muscular System: Female

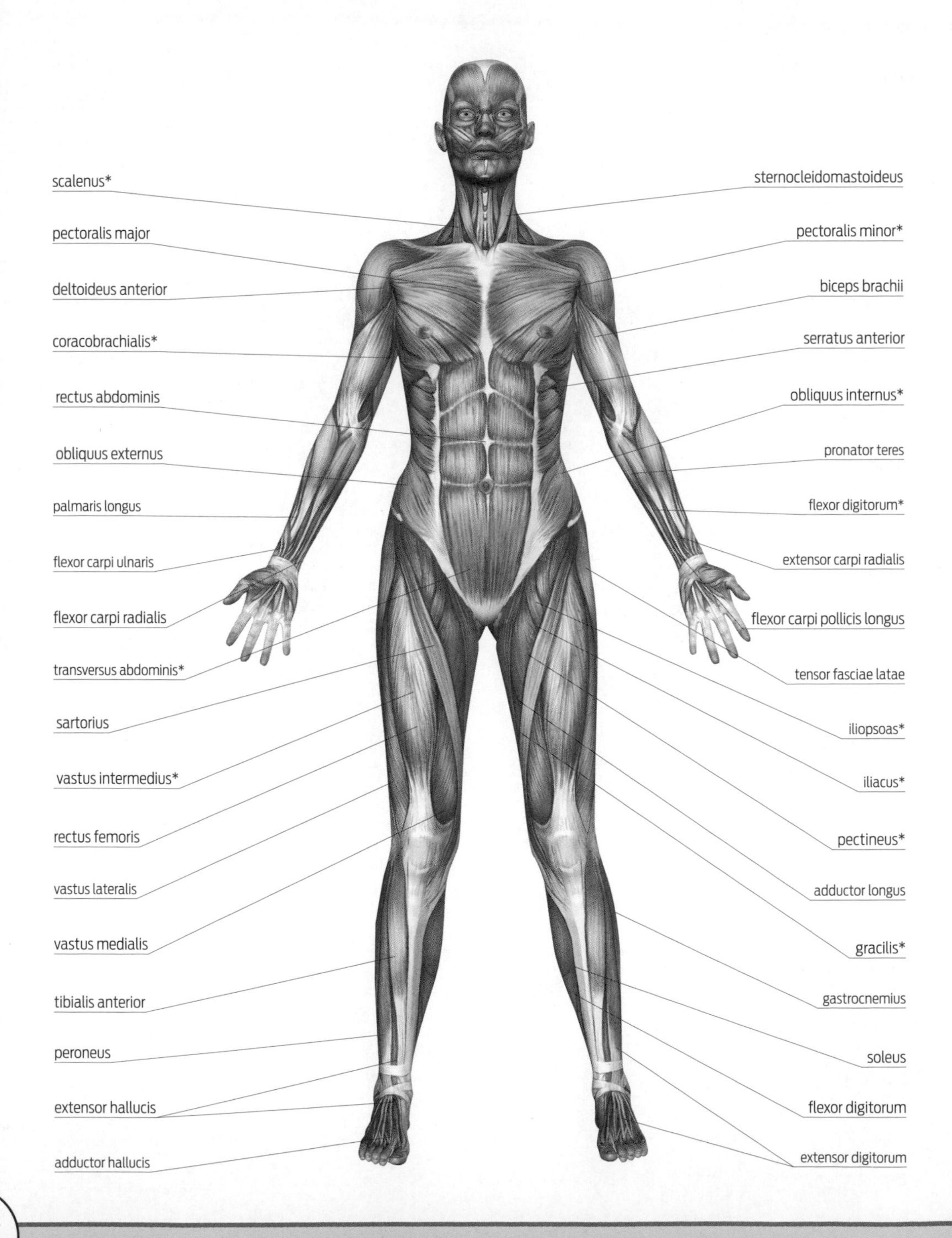

Annotation Key
* Indicates deep muscles

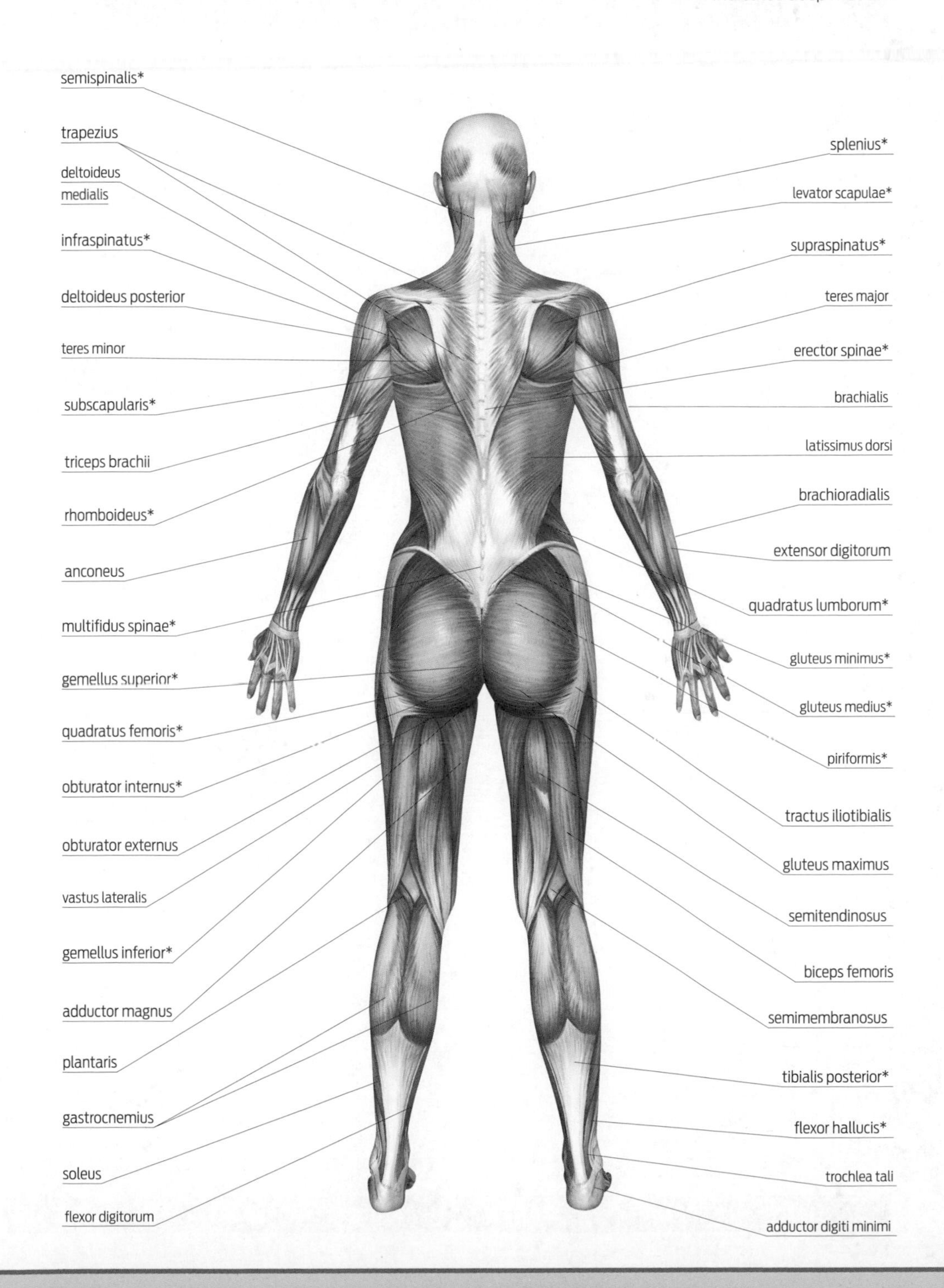

Twelve-Month Planner

	JANUARY	FEBRUARY	MARCH	APRIL	MAY	JUNE
1						
2						
3						
4						
5						
6						
7						
8						
9						
10						
11						
12						
13						
14						
15						
16						
17						
18						
19						
20						
21						
22						
23						
24						
25						
26						
27						
28						
29						
30						
31						

| | JANUARY | FEBRUARY | MARCH | APRIL | MAY | JUNE |

JULY	AUGUST	SEPTEMBER	OCTOBER	NOVEMBER	DECEMBER	
						1
						2
						3
						4
						5
						6
						7
						8
						9
						10
						11
						12
						13
						14
						15
						16
						17
						18
						19
						20
						21
						22
						23
						24
						25
						26
						27
						28
						29
						30
						31
JULY	AUGUST	SEPTEMBER	OCTOBER	NOVEMBER	DECEMBER	

Start-of-Year Assessment

DATE ___ / ___ / ___ AGE ___ HEIGHT ___

Current Physical Measurements	
Weight	
BMI	
Waist–hip ratio	
Chest, relaxed	
Chest, expanded	
Waist	
Stomach	
Hips	
Neck	
Shoulders	
Right upper arm, relaxed	
Right upper arm, flexed	
Left upper arm, relaxed	
Left upper arm, flexed	
Right forearm, relaxed	
Right forearm, flexed	
Left forearm, relaxed	
Left forearm, flexed	
Right upper thigh	
Right lower thigh	
Left upper thigh	
Left lower thigh	
Right calf	
Left calf	

Physical Measurement Targets	
Weight	
BMI	
Waist–hip ratio	
Chest, relaxed	
Chest, expanded	
Waist	
Stomach	
Hips	
Neck	
Shoulders	
Right upper arm, relaxed	
Right upper arm, flexed	
Left upper arm, relaxed	
Left upper arm, flexed	
Right forearm, relaxed	
Right forearm, flexed	
Left forearm, relaxed	
Left forearm, flexed	
Right upper thigh	
Right lower thigh	
Left upper thigh	
Left lower thigh	
Right calf	
Left calf	

Time how long it takes to run 1 mile/2km.	Current		Target	
Count how many push-ups you can do before you have to stop.	Current		Target	
Count how many sit-ups you can do before you have to stop.	Current		Target	
Count how many squats you can do before you have to stop.	Current		Target	
Sit with legs out straight. Place a ruler on the floor with the tip between your feet. Record how many inches/cm you stretch up to or beyond your feet.	Current distance [+/-]		Target distance [+/-]	
Time you can balance on one foot: right leg left leg	Current		Target	

Cardiovascular Fitness Test

Use the same course each time. It should take about 12 minutes to complete the first test, regardless of whether you walk or run.

- Record your resting heart rate before warming up
- Complete the course as fast as you can, recording your working heart rate every 3 minutes
- Still standing, record your recovery heart rate when you finish and then 1, 2, and 3 minutes after you finish
- Record the time it took to finish the course.

Cardiovascular Fitness Test			
		Current	Target
Resting heart rate			
Working heart rate:	after 3 minutes		
	after 6 minutes		
	after 9 minutes		
Recovery heart rate:	at course completion		
	1 minute after completion		
	2 minutes after completion		
	3 minutes after completion		
Completion time			

Current Personal Summary

Strength level (1–5) ☐

Endurance level (1–5) ☐

Satisfaction with fitness (1–5) ☐

Satisfaction with weight (1–5) ☐

Quality of diet (1–5) ☐

Energy level (1–5) ☐

Sleep quality (1–5) ☐

Stress level (1–5) ☐

Mood level (1–5) ☐

Personal Goals

Week Beginning

/ /

Planned exercise sessions this week

	Exercise	Completed [Y/N]
Monday		
Tuesday		
Wednesday		
Thursday		
Friday		
Saturday		
Sunday		

Strength Training

	Focus area	Equipment	SET 1		SET 2		SET 3		SET 4	
			Weight	Reps	Weight	Reps	Weight	Reps	Weight	Reps
MONDAY										

	Focus area	Equipment	SET 1		SET 2		SET 3		SET 4	
			Weight	Reps	Weight	Reps	Weight	Reps	Weight	Reps
TUESDAY										

	Focus area	Equipment	SET 1		SET 2		SET 3		SET 4	
			Weight	Reps	Weight	Reps	Weight	Reps	Weight	Reps
WEDNESDAY										

	Focus area	Equipment	SET 1		SET 2		SET 3		SET 4	
			Weight	Reps	Weight	Reps	Weight	Reps	Weight	Reps
THURSDAY										

	Focus area	Equipment	SET 1		SET 2		SET 3		SET 4	
			Weight	Reps	Weight	Reps	Weight	Reps	Weight	Reps
FRIDAY										

	Focus area	Equipment	SET 1		SET 2		SET 3		SET 4	
			Weight	Reps	Weight	Reps	Weight	Reps	Weight	Reps
SATURDAY										

	Focus area	Equipment	SET 1		SET 2		SET 3		SET 4	
			Weight	Reps	Weight	Reps	Weight	Reps	Weight	Reps
SUNDAY										

Cardio Training

MONDAY	Exercise	Time	Distance/ resistance	Intensity	Heart rate	Ease	Cal/kJ expended
							Total:

TUESDAY	Exercise	Time	Distance/ resistance	Intensity	Heart rate	Ease	Cal/kJ expended
							Total:

WEDNESDAY	Exercise	Time	Distance/ resistance	Intensity	Heart rate	Ease	Cal/kJ expended
							Total:

THURSDAY	Exercise	Time	Distance/ resistance	Intensity	Heart rate	Ease	Cal/kJ expended
							Total:

FRIDAY	Exercise	Time	Distance/ resistance	Intensity	Heart rate	Ease	Cal/kJ expended
							Total:

SATURDAY	Exercise	Time	Distance/ resistance	Intensity	Heart rate	Ease	Cal/kJ expended
							Total:

SUNDAY	Exercise	Time	Distance/ resistance	Intensity	Heart rate	Ease	Cal/kJ expended
							Total:
							Weekly Total:

Food Diary

MONDAY		Cal/kJ	Fat	Protein	Carbs
Breakfast time: am/pm					
Lunch time: am/pm					
Dinner time: am/pm					
Snacks:					
Coffees/teas:	Fluid intake: **Totals:**				

TUESDAY		Cal/kJ	Fat	Protein	Carbs
Breakfast time: am/pm					
Lunch time: am/pm					
Dinner time: am/pm					
Snacks:					
Coffees/teas:	Fluid intake: **Totals:**				

WEDNESDAY		Cal/kJ	Fat	Protein	Carbs
Breakfast time: am/pm					
Lunch time: am/pm					
Dinner time: am/pm					
Snacks:					
Coffees/teas:	Fluid intake: **Totals:**				

THURSDAY		Cal/kJ	Fat	Protein	Carbs
Breakfast time: am/pm					
Lunch time: am/pm					
Dinner time: am/pm					
Snacks:					
Coffees/teas:	Fluid intake: **Totals:**				

FRIDAY		Cal/kJ	Fat	Protein	Carbs
Breakfast time: am/pm					
Lunch time: am/pm					
Dinner time: am/pm					
Snacks:					
Coffees/teas:	Fluid intake: **Totals:**				

SATURDAY		Cal/kJ	Fat	Protein	Carbs
Breakfast time: am/pm					
Lunch time: am/pm					
Dinner time: am/pm					
Snacks:					
Coffees/teas:	Fluid intake: **Totals:**				

SUNDAY		Cal/kJ	Fat	Protein	Carbs
Breakfast time: am/pm					
Lunch time: am/pm					
Dinner time: am/pm					
Snacks:					
Coffees/teas:	Fluid intake: **Totals:**				

Units of alcohol this week: Total alcohol Cal/kJ:

Vitamins and supplements

Weekly Totals	Cal/kJ	Fat	Protein	Carbs

Weekly Personal Summary

Energy level (1–5)

Stress level (1–5)

Hours of sleep

Sleep quality (1–5)

Mood (1–5)

Appetite (1–5)

Cal/kJ intake

Planned Cal/kJ	
Actual Cal/kJ	

Difference [+/-]

Weight at start of week

Weight at end of week

BMI at start of week

BMI at end of week

Injuries or illnesses

Week Beginning

/ /

Planned exercise sessions this week

	Exercise	Completed [Y/N]
Monday		
Tuesday		
Wednesday		
Thursday		
Friday		
Saturday		
Sunday		

Strength Training

MONDAY

ocus area	Equipment	SET 1		SET 2		SET 3		SET 4	
		Weight	Reps	Weight	Reps	Weight	Reps	Weight	Reps

TUESDAY

ocus area	Equipment	SET 1		SET 2		SET 3		SET 4	
		Weight	Reps	Weight	Reps	Weight	Reps	Weight	Reps

WEDNESDAY

ocus area	Equipment	SET 1		SET 2		SET 3		SET 4	
		Weight	Reps	Weight	Reps	Weight	Reps	Weight	Reps

THURSDAY

ocus area	Equipment	SET 1		SET 2		SET 3		SET 4	
		Weight	Reps	Weight	Reps	Weight	Reps	Weight	Reps

FRIDAY

ocus area	Equipment	SET 1		SET 2		SET 3		SET 4	
		Weight	Reps	Weight	Reps	Weight	Reps	Weight	Reps

SATURDAY

Focus area	Equipment	SET 1		SET 2		SET 3		SET 4	
		Weight	Reps	Weight	Reps	Weight	Reps	Weight	Reps

SUNDAY

Focus area	Equipment	SET 1		SET 2		SET 3		SET 4	
		Weight	Reps	Weight	Reps	Weight	Reps	Weight	Reps

Cardio Training

MONDAY

Exercise	Time	Distance/ resistance	Intensity	Heart rate	Ease	Cal/kJ expended

Total:

TUESDAY

Exercise	Time	Distance/ resistance	Intensity	Heart rate	Ease	Cal/kJ expended

Total:

WEDNESDAY

Exercise	Time	Distance/ resistance	Intensity	Heart rate	Ease	Cal/kJ expended

Total:

THURSDAY

Exercise	Time	Distance/ resistance	Intensity	Heart rate	Ease	Cal/kJ expended

Total:

FRIDAY

Exercise	Time	Distance/ resistance	Intensity	Heart rate	Ease	Cal/kJ expended

Total:

SATURDAY

Exercise	Time	Distance/ resistance	Intensity	Heart rate	Ease	Cal/kJ expended

Total:

SUNDAY

Exercise	Time	Distance/ resistance	Intensity	Heart rate	Ease	Cal/kJ expended

Total:

Weekly Total:

Food Diary

MONDAY			Cal/kJ	Fat	Protein	Carbs
Breakfast time: am/pm						
Lunch time: am/pm						
Dinner time: am/pm						
Snacks:						
Coffees/teas:	Fluid intake:	**Totals:**				

TUESDAY			Cal/kJ	Fat	Protein	Carbs
Breakfast time: am/pm						
Lunch time: am/pm						
Dinner time: am/pm						
Snacks:						
Coffees/teas:	Fluid intake:	**Totals:**				

WEDNESDAY			Cal/kJ	Fat	Protein	Carbs
Breakfast time: am/pm						
Lunch time: am/pm						
Dinner time: am/pm						
Snacks:						
Coffees/teas:	Fluid intake:	**Totals:**				

THURSDAY			Cal/kJ	Fat	Protein	Carbs
Breakfast time: am/pm						
Lunch time: am/pm						
Dinner time: am/pm						
Snacks:						
Coffees/teas:	Fluid intake:	**Totals:**				

FRIDAY			Cal/kJ	Fat	Protein	Carbs
Breakfast time: am/pm						
Lunch time: am/pm						
Dinner time: am/pm						
Snacks:						
Coffees/teas:	Fluid intake:	**Totals:**				

SATURDAY			Cal/kJ	Fat	Protein	Carbs
Breakfast time: am/pm						
Lunch time: am/pm						
Dinner time: am/pm						
Snacks:						
Coffees/teas:	Fluid intake:	**Totals:**				

SUNDAY			Cal/kJ	Fat	Protein	Carbs
Breakfast time: am/pm						
Lunch time: am/pm						
Dinner time: am/pm						
Snacks:						
Coffees/teas:	Fluid intake:	**Totals:**				

Units of alcohol this week: ____ Total alcohol Cal/kJ: ____

Vitamins and supplements

Weekly Totals	Cal/kJ	Fat	Protein	Carbs

Weekly Personal Summary

Energy level (1–5) ____ Stress level (1–5) ____

Hours of sleep ____ Sleep quality (1–5) ____

Mood (1–5) ____ Appetite (1–5) ____

Cal/kJ intake

Planned Cal/kJ	
Actual Cal/kJ	
Difference [+/-]	

Weight at start of week ____

Weight at end of week ____

BMI at start of week ____

BMI at end of week ____

Injuries or illnesses ____

Week Beginning

/ /

Planned exercise sessions this week

	Exercise	Completed [Y/N]
Monday		
Tuesday		
Wednesday		
Thursday		
Friday		
Saturday		
Sunday		

Strength Training

MONDAY

Focus area	Equipment	SET 1		SET 2		SET 3		SET 4	
		Weight	Reps	Weight	Reps	Weight	Reps	Weight	Reps

TUESDAY

Focus area	Equipment	SET 1		SET 2		SET 3		SET 4	
		Weight	Reps	Weight	Reps	Weight	Reps	Weight	Reps

WEDNESDAY

Focus area	Equipment	SET 1		SET 2		SET 3		SET 4	
		Weight	Reps	Weight	Reps	Weight	Reps	Weight	Reps

THURSDAY

Focus area	Equipment	SET 1		SET 2		SET 3		SET 4	
		Weight	Reps	Weight	Reps	Weight	Reps	Weight	Reps

FRIDAY

Focus area	Equipment	SET 1		SET 2		SET 3		SET 4	
		Weight	Reps	Weight	Reps	Weight	Reps	Weight	Reps

SATURDAY

Focus area	Equipment	SET 1		SET 2		SET 3		SET 4	
		Weight	Reps	Weight	Reps	Weight	Reps	Weight	Reps

SUNDAY

Focus area	Equipment	SET 1		SET 2		SET 3		SET 4	
		Weight	Reps	Weight	Reps	Weight	Reps	Weight	Reps

Cardio Training

MONDAY

Exercise	Time	Distance/ resistance	Intensity	Heart rate	Ease	Cal/kJ expended
						Total:

TUESDAY

Exercise	Time	Distance/ resistance	Intensity	Heart rate	Ease	Cal/kJ expended
						Total:

WEDNESDAY

Exercise	Time	Distance/ resistance	Intensity	Heart rate	Ease	Cal/kJ expended
						Total:

THURSDAY

Exercise	Time	Distance/ resistance	Intensity	Heart rate	Ease	Cal/kJ expended
						Total:

FRIDAY

Exercise	Time	Distance/ resistance	Intensity	Heart rate	Ease	Cal/kJ expended
						Total:

SATURDAY

Exercise	Time	Distance/ resistance	Intensity	Heart rate	Ease	Cal/kJ expended
						Total:

SUNDAY

Exercise	Time	Distance/ resistance	Intensity	Heart rate	Ease	Cal/kJ expended
						Total:
						Weekly Total:

Food Diary

MONDAY			Cal/kJ	Fat	Protein	Carbs
Breakfast time: am/pm						
Lunch time: am/pm						
Dinner time: am/pm						
Snacks:						
Coffees/teas:	Fluid intake:	**Totals:**				

TUESDAY			Cal/kJ	Fat	Protein	Carbs
Breakfast time: am/pm						
Lunch time: am/pm						
Dinner time: am/pm						
Snacks:						
Coffees/teas:	Fluid intake:	**Totals:**				

WEDNESDAY			Cal/kJ	Fat	Protein	Carbs
Breakfast time: am/pm						
Lunch time: am/pm						
Dinner time: am/pm						
Snacks:						
Coffees/teas:	Fluid intake:	**Totals:**				

THURSDAY			Cal/kJ	Fat	Protein	Carbs
Breakfast time: am/pm						
Lunch time: am/pm						
Dinner time: am/pm						
Snacks:						
Coffees/teas:	Fluid intake:	**Totals:**				

FRIDAY		Cal/kJ	Fat	Protein	Carbs
Breakfast time: am/pm					
Lunch time: am/pm					
Dinner time: am/pm					
Snacks:					
Coffees/teas:	Fluid intake: **Totals:**				

SATURDAY		Cal/kJ	Fat	Protein	Carbs
Breakfast time: am/pm					
Lunch time: am/pm					
Dinner time: am/pm					
Snacks:					
Coffees/teas:	Fluid intake: **Totals:**				

SUNDAY		Cal/kJ	Fat	Protein	Carbs
Breakfast time: am/pm					
Lunch time: am/pm					
Dinner time: am/pm					
Snacks:					
Coffees/teas:	Fluid intake: **Totals:**				

Units of alcohol this week: Total alcohol Cal/kJ:

Vitamins and supplements

Weekly Totals	Cal/kJ	Fat	Protein	Carbs

Weekly Personal Summary

Energy level 1–5

Stress level 1–5

Hours of sleep

Sleep quality 1–5

Mood 1–5

Appetite 1–5

Cal/kJ intake

Planned Cal/kJ	
Actual Cal/kJ	

Difference [+/-]

Weight at start of week

Weight at end of week

BMI at start of week

BMI at end of week

Injuries or illnesses

Week Beginning

/ /

Planned exercise sessions this week

	Exercise	Completed [Y/N]
Monday		
Tuesday		
Wednesday		
Thursday		
Friday		
Saturday		
Sunday		

Strength Training

MONDAY	Focus area	Equipment	SET 1		SET 2		SET 3		SET 4	
			Weight	Reps	Weight	Reps	Weight	Reps	Weight	Reps

TUESDAY	Focus area	Equipment	SET 1		SET 2		SET 3		SET 4	
			Weight	Reps	Weight	Reps	Weight	Reps	Weight	Reps

WEDNESDAY	Focus area	Equipment	SET 1		SET 2		SET 3		SET 4	
			Weight	Reps	Weight	Reps	Weight	Reps	Weight	Reps

THURSDAY	Focus area	Equipment	SET 1		SET 2		SET 3		SET 4	
			Weight	Reps	Weight	Reps	Weight	Reps	Weight	Reps

FRIDAY	Focus area	Equipment	SET 1		SET 2		SET 3		SET 4	
			Weight	Reps	Weight	Reps	Weight	Reps	Weight	Reps

SATURDAY	Focus area	Equipment	SET 1		SET 2		SET 3		SET 4	
			Weight	Reps	Weight	Reps	Weight	Reps	Weight	Reps

SUNDAY	Focus area	Equipment	SET 1		SET 2		SET 3		SET 4	
			Weight	Reps	Weight	Reps	Weight	Reps	Weight	Reps

Cardio Training

MONDAY

Exercise	Time	Distance/ resistance	Intensity	Heart rate	Ease	Cal/kJ expended
						Total:

TUESDAY

Exercise	Time	Distance/ resistance	Intensity	Heart rate	Ease	Cal/kJ expended
						Total:

WEDNESDAY

Exercise	Time	Distance/ resistance	Intensity	Heart rate	Ease	Cal/kJ expended
						Total:

THURSDAY

Exercise	Time	Distance/ resistance	Intensity	Heart rate	Ease	Cal/kJ expended
						Total:

FRIDAY

Exercise	Time	Distance/ resistance	Intensity	Heart rate	Ease	Cal/kJ expended
						Total:

SATURDAY

Exercise	Time	Distance/ resistance	Intensity	Heart rate	Ease	Cal/kJ expended
						Total:

SUNDAY

Exercise	Time	Distance/ resistance	Intensity	Heart rate	Ease	Cal/kJ expended
						Total:
						Weekly Total:

Food Diary

MONDAY		Cal/kJ	Fat	Protein	Carbs
Breakfast time: am/pm					
Lunch time: am/pm					
Dinner time: am/pm					
Snacks:					
Coffees/teas:	Fluid intake: **Totals:**				

TUESDAY		Cal/kJ	Fat	Protein	Carbs
Breakfast time: am/pm					
Lunch time: am/pm					
Dinner time: am/pm					
Snacks:					
Coffees/teas:	Fluid intake: **Totals:**				

WEDNESDAY		Cal/kJ	Fat	Protein	Carbs
Breakfast time: am/pm					
Lunch time: am/pm					
Dinner time: am/pm					
Snacks:					
Coffees/teas:	Fluid intake: **Totals:**				

THURSDAY		Cal/kJ	Fat	Protein	Carbs
Breakfast time: am/pm					
Lunch time: am/pm					
Dinner time: am/pm					
Snacks:					
Coffees/teas:	Fluid intake: **Totals:**				

FRIDAY		Cal/kJ	Fat	Protein	Carbs
Breakfast time: am/pm					
Lunch time: am/pm					
Dinner time: am/pm					
Snacks:					
Coffees/teas:	Fluid intake: **Totals:**				

SATURDAY		Cal/kJ	Fat	Protein	Carbs
Breakfast time: am/pm					
Lunch time: am/pm					
Dinner time: am/pm					
Snacks:					
Coffees/teas:	Fluid intake: **Totals:**				

SUNDAY		Cal/kJ	Fat	Protein	Carbs
Breakfast time: am/pm					
Lunch time: am/pm					
Dinner time: am/pm					
Snacks:					
Coffees/teas:	Fluid intake: **Totals:**				

Units of alcohol this week: Total alcohol Cal/kJ:

Vitamins and supplements

Weekly Totals	Cal/kJ	Fat	Protein	Carbs

Weekly Personal Summary

Energy level (1–5)

Stress level (1–5)

Hours of sleep

Sleep quality (1–5)

Mood (1–5)

Appetite (1–5)

Cal/kJ intake

Planned Cal/kJ

Actual Cal/kJ

Difference [+/-]

Weight at start of week

Weight at end of week

BMI at start of week

BMI at end of week

Injuries or illnesses

Week Beginning

/ /

Planned exercise sessions this week

	Exercise	Completed [Y/N]
Monday		
Tuesday		
Wednesday		
Thursday		
Friday		
Saturday		
Sunday		

Strength Training

MONDAY

ocus area	Equipment	SET 1		SET 2		SET 3		SET 4	
		Weight	Reps	Weight	Reps	Weight	Reps	Weight	Reps

TUESDAY

ocus area	Equipment	SET 1		SET 2		SET 3		SET 4	
		Weight	Reps	Weight	Reps	Weight	Reps	Weight	Reps

WEDNESDAY

ocus area	Equipment	SET 1		SET 2		SET 3		SET 4	
		Weight	Reps	Weight	Reps	Weight	Reps	Weight	Reps

THURSDAY

ocus area	Equipment	SET 1		SET 2		SET 3		SET 4	
		Weight	Reps	Weight	Reps	Weight	Reps	Weight	Reps

FRIDAY

ocus area	Equipment	SET 1		SET 2		SET 3		SET 4	
		Weight	Reps	Weight	Reps	Weight	Reps	Weight	Reps

SATURDAY

ocus area	Equipment	SET 1		SET 2		SET 3		SET 4	
		Weight	Reps	Weight	Reps	Weight	Reps	Weight	Reps

SUNDAY

ocus area	Equipment	SET 1		SET 2		SET 3		SET 4	
		Weight	Reps	Weight	Reps	Weight	Reps	Weight	Reps

Cardio Training

MONDAY

Exercise	Time	Distance/ resistance	Intensity	Heart rate	Ease	Cal/kJ expended
						Total:

TUESDAY

Exercise	Time	Distance/ resistance	Intensity	Heart rate	Ease	Cal/kJ expended
						Total:

WEDNESDAY

Exercise	Time	Distance/ resistance	Intensity	Heart rate	Ease	Cal/kJ expended
						Total:

THURSDAY

Exercise	Time	Distance/ resistance	Intensity	Heart rate	Ease	Cal/kJ expended
						Total:

FRIDAY

Exercise	Time	Distance/ resistance	Intensity	Heart rate	Ease	Cal/kJ expended
						Total:

SATURDAY

Exercise	Time	Distance/ resistance	Intensity	Heart rate	Ease	Cal/kJ expended
						Total:

SUNDAY

Exercise	Time	Distance/ resistance	Intensity	Heart rate	Ease	Cal/kJ expended
						Total:
						Weekly Total:

Food Diary

MONDAY			Cal/kJ	Fat	Protein	Carbs
Breakfast time: am/pm						
Lunch time: am/pm						
Dinner time: am/pm						
Snacks:						
Coffees/teas:	Fluid intake:	**Totals:**				

TUESDAY			Cal/kJ	Fat	Protein	Carbs
Breakfast time: am/pm						
Lunch time: am/pm						
Dinner time: am/pm						
Snacks:						
Coffees/teas:	Fluid intake:	**Totals:**				

WEDNESDAY			Cal/kJ	Fat	Protein	Carbs
Breakfast time: am/pm						
Lunch time: am/pm						
Dinner time: am/pm						
Snacks:						
Coffees/teas:	Fluid intake:	**Totals:**				

THURSDAY			Cal/kJ	Fat	Protein	Carbs
Breakfast time: am/pm						
Lunch time: am/pm						
Dinner time: am/pm						
Snacks:						
Coffees/teas:	Fluid intake:	**Totals:**				

FRIDAY		Cal/kJ	Fat	Protein	Carbs
Breakfast time: am/pm					
Lunch time: am/pm					
Dinner time: am/pm					
Snacks:					
Coffees/teas:	Fluid intake: **Totals:**				

SATURDAY		Cal/kJ	Fat	Protein	Carbs
Breakfast time: am/pm					
Lunch time: am/pm					
Dinner time: am/pm					
Snacks:					
Coffees/teas:	Fluid intake: **Totals:**				

SUNDAY		Cal/kJ	Fat	Protein	Carbs
Breakfast time: am/pm					
Lunch time: am/pm					
Dinner time: am/pm					
Snacks:					
Coffees/teas:	Fluid intake: **Totals:**				

Units of alcohol this week: Total alcohol Cal/kJ:

Vitamins and supplements

Weekly Totals	Cal/kJ	Fat	Protein	Carbs

Weekly Personal Summary

Energy level (1–5) Stress level (1–5)

Hours of sleep Sleep quality (1–5)

Mood (1–5) Appetite (1–5)

Cal/kJ intake

Planned Cal/kJ	
Actual Cal/kJ	
Difference [+/-]	

Weight at start of week

Weight at end of week

BMI at start of week

BMI at end of week

Injuries or illnesses

Week Beginning

/ /

Planned exercise sessions this week

	Exercise	Completed [Y/N]
Monday		
Tuesday		
Wednesday		
Thursday		
Friday		
Saturday		
Sunday		

Strength Training

	ocus area	Equipment	SET 1		SET 2		SET 3		SET 4	
			Weight	Reps	Weight	Reps	Weight	Reps	Weight	Reps
MONDAY										

	ocus area	Equipment	SET 1		SET 2		SET 3		SET 4	
			Weight	Reps	Weight	Reps	Weight	Reps	Weight	Reps
TUESDAY										

	ocus area	Equipment	SET 1		SET 2		SET 3		SET 4	
			Weight	Reps	Weight	Reps	Weight	Reps	Weight	Reps
WEDNESDAY										

	ocus area	Equipment	SET 1		SET 2		SET 3		SET 4	
			Weight	Reps	Weight	Reps	Weight	Reps	Weight	Reps
THURSDAY										

	ocus area	Equipment	SET 1		SET 2		SET 3		SET 4	
			Weight	Reps	Weight	Reps	Weight	Reps	Weight	Reps
FRIDAY										

	ocus area	Equipment	SET 1		SET 2		SET 3		SET 4	
			Weight	Reps	Weight	Reps	Weight	Reps	Weight	Reps
SATURDAY										

	ocus area	Equipment	SET 1		SET 2		SET 3		SET 4	
			Weight	Reps	Weight	Reps	Weight	Reps	Weight	Reps
SUNDAY										

Cardio Training

MONDAY	Exercise	Time	Distance/ resistance	Intensity	Heart rate	Ease	Cal/kJ expended
							Total:

TUESDAY	Exercise	Time	Distance/ resistance	Intensity	Heart rate	Ease	Cal/kJ expended
							Total:

WEDNESDAY	Exercise	Time	Distance/ resistance	Intensity	Heart rate	Ease	Cal/kJ expended
							Total:

THURSDAY	Exercise	Time	Distance/ resistance	Intensity	Heart rate	Ease	Cal/kJ expended
							Total:

FRIDAY	Exercise	Time	Distance/ resistance	Intensity	Heart rate	Ease	Cal/kJ expended
							Total:

SATURDAY	Exercise	Time	Distance/ resistance	Intensity	Heart rate	Ease	Cal/kJ expended
							Total:

SUNDAY	Exercise	Time	Distance/ resistance	Intensity	Heart rate	Ease	Cal/kJ expended
							Total:
							Weekly Total:

Food Diary

MONDAY		Cal/kJ	Fat	Protein	Carbs
Breakfast time: am/pm					
Lunch time: am/pm					
Dinner time: am/pm					
Snacks:					
Coffees/teas:	Fluid intake: **Totals:**				

TUESDAY		Cal/kJ	Fat	Protein	Carbs
Breakfast time: am/pm					
Lunch time: am/pm					
Dinner time: am/pm					
Snacks:					
Coffees/teas:	Fluid intake: **Totals:**				

WEDNESDAY		Cal/kJ	Fat	Protein	Carbs
Breakfast time: am/pm					
Lunch time: am/pm					
Dinner time: am/pm					
Snacks:					
Coffees/teas:	Fluid intake: **Totals:**				

THURSDAY		Cal/kJ	Fat	Protein	Carbs
Breakfast time: am/pm					
Lunch time: am/pm					
Dinner time: am/pm					
Snacks:					
Coffees/teas:	Fluid intake: **Totals:**				

FRIDAY		Cal/kJ	Fat	Protein	Carbs
Breakfast time: am/pm					
Lunch time: am/pm					
Dinner time: am/pm					
Snacks:					
Coffees/teas:	Fluid intake: **Totals:**				

SATURDAY		Cal/kJ	Fat	Protein	Carbs
Breakfast time: am/pm					
Lunch time: am/pm					
Dinner time: am/pm					
Snacks:					
Coffees/teas:	Fluid intake: **Totals:**				

SUNDAY		Cal/kJ	Fat	Protein	Carbs
Breakfast time: am/pm					
Lunch time: am/pm					
Dinner time: am/pm					
Snacks:					
Coffees/teas:	Fluid intake: **Totals:**				

Units of alcohol this week: ____ Total alcohol Cal/kJ: ____

Vitamins and supplements

Weekly Totals	Cal/kJ	Fat	Protein	Carbs

Weekly Personal Summary

Energy level (1–5) ____ Stress level (1–5) ____

Hours of sleep ____ Sleep quality (1–5) ____

Mood (1–5) ____ Appetite (1–5) ____

Cal/kJ intake

Planned Cal/kJ	
Actual Cal/kJ	
Difference [+/-]	

Weight at start of week ____

Weight at end of week ____

BMI at start of week ____

BMI at end of week ____

Injuries or illnesses ____

Week Beginning

/ /

Planned exercise sessions this week

	Exercise	Completed [Y/N]
Monday		
Tuesday		
Wednesday		
Thursday		
Friday		
Saturday		
Sunday		

Strength Training

MONDAY	ocus area	Equipment	SET 1		SET 2		SET 3		SET 4	
			Weight	Reps	Weight	Reps	Weight	Reps	Weight	Reps

TUESDAY	ocus area	Equipment	SET 1		SET 2		SET 3		SET 4	
			Weight	Reps	Weight	Reps	Weight	Reps	Weight	Reps

WEDNESDAY	ocus area	Equipment	SET 1		SET 2		SET 3		SET 4	
			Weight	Reps	Weight	Reps	Weight	Reps	Weight	Reps

THURSDAY	ocus area	Equipment	SET 1		SET 2		SET 3		SET 4	
			Weight	Reps	Weight	Reps	Weight	Reps	Weight	Reps

FRIDAY	ocus area	Equipment	SET 1		SET 2		SET 3		SET 4	
			Weight	Reps	Weight	Reps	Weight	Reps	Weight	Reps

SATURDAY	ocus area	Equipment	SET 1		SET 2		SET 3		SET 4	
			Weight	Reps	Weight	Reps	Weight	Reps	Weight	Reps

SUNDAY	ocus area	Equipment	SET 1		SET 2		SET 3		SET 4	
			Weight	Reps	Weight	Reps	Weight	Reps	Weight	Reps

Cardio Training

MONDAY	Exercise	Time	Distance/ resistance	Intensity	Heart rate	Ease	Cal/kJ expended
							Total:

TUESDAY	Exercise	Time	Distance/ resistance	Intensity	Heart rate	Ease	Cal/kJ expended
							Total:

WEDNESDAY	Exercise	Time	Distance/ resistance	Intensity	Heart rate	Ease	Cal/kJ expended
							Total:

THURSDAY	Exercise	Time	Distance/ resistance	Intensity	Heart rate	Ease	Cal/kJ expended
							Total:

FRIDAY	Exercise	Time	Distance/ resistance	Intensity	Heart rate	Ease	Cal/kJ expended
							Total:

SATURDAY	Exercise	Time	Distance/ resistance	Intensity	Heart rate	Ease	Cal/kJ expended
							Total:

SUNDAY	Exercise	Time	Distance/ resistance	Intensity	Heart rate	Ease	Cal/kJ expended
							Total:
							Weekly Total:

Food Diary

MONDAY		Cal/kJ	Fat	Protein	Carbs
Breakfast time: am/pm					
Lunch time: am/pm					
Dinner time: am/pm					
Snacks:					
Coffees/teas:	Fluid intake: **Totals:**				

TUESDAY		Cal/kJ	Fat	Protein	Carbs
Breakfast time: am/pm					
Lunch time: am/pm					
Dinner time: am/pm					
Snacks:					
Coffees/teas:	Fluid intake: **Totals:**				

WEDNESDAY		Cal/kJ	Fat	Protein	Carbs
Breakfast time: am/pm					
Lunch time: am/pm					
Dinner time: am/pm					
Snacks:					
Coffees/teas:	Fluid intake: **Totals:**				

THURSDAY		Cal/kJ	Fat	Protein	Carbs
Breakfast time: am/pm					
Lunch time: am/pm					
Dinner time: am/pm					
Snacks:					
Coffees/teas:	Fluid intake: **Totals:**				

FRIDAY			Cal/kJ	Fat	Protein	Carbs
Breakfast time: am/pm						
Lunch time: am/pm						
Dinner time: am/pm						
Snacks:						
Coffees/teas:	Fluid intake:	Totals:				

SATURDAY			Cal/kJ	Fat	Protein	Carbs
Breakfast time: am/pm						
Lunch time: am/pm						
Dinner time: am/pm						
Snacks:						
Coffees/teas:	Fluid intake:	Totals:				

SUNDAY			Cal/kJ	Fat	Protein	Carbs
Breakfast time: am/pm						
Lunch time: am/pm						
Dinner time: am/pm						
Snacks:						
Coffees/teas:	Fluid intake:	Totals:				

Units of alcohol this week: Total alcohol Cal/kJ:

Vitamins and supplements

Weekly Totals	Cal/kJ	Fat	Protein	Carbs

Weekly Personal Summary

Energy level (1–5)

Stress level (1–5)

Hours of sleep

Sleep quality (1–5)

Mood (1–5)

Appetite (1–5)

Cal/kJ intake

Planned Cal/kJ	
Actual Cal/kJ	
Difference [+/-]	

Weight at start of week

Weight at end of week

BMI at start of week

BMI at end of week

Injuries or illnesses

Week Beginning

/ /

Planned exercise sessions this week

	Exercise	Completed [Y/N]
Monday		
Tuesday		
Wednesday		
Thursday		
Friday		
Saturday		
Sunday		

Strength Training

MONDAY	Focus area	Equipment	SET 1		SET 2		SET 3		SET 4	
			Weight	Reps	Weight	Reps	Weight	Reps	Weight	Reps

TUESDAY	Focus area	Equipment	SET 1		SET 2		SET 3		SET 4	
			Weight	Reps	Weight	Reps	Weight	Reps	Weight	Reps

WEDNESDAY	Focus area	Equipment	SET 1		SET 2		SET 3		SET 4	
			Weight	Reps	Weight	Reps	Weight	Reps	Weight	Reps

THURSDAY	Focus area	Equipment	SET 1		SET 2		SET 3		SET 4	
			Weight	Reps	Weight	Reps	Weight	Reps	Weight	Reps

FRIDAY	Focus area	Equipment	SET 1		SET 2		SET 3		SET 4	
			Weight	Reps	Weight	Reps	Weight	Reps	Weight	Reps

SATURDAY	Focus area	Equipment	SET 1		SET 2		SET 3		SET 4	
			Weight	Reps	Weight	Reps	Weight	Reps	Weight	Reps

SUNDAY	Focus area	Equipment	SET 1		SET 2		SET 3		SET 4	
			Weight	Reps	Weight	Reps	Weight	Reps	Weight	Reps

Cardio Training

MONDAY	Exercise	Time	Distance/ resistance	Intensity	Heart rate	Ease	Cal/kJ expended
							Total:

TUESDAY	Exercise	Time	Distance/ resistance	Intensity	Heart rate	Ease	Cal/kJ expended
							Total:

WEDNESDAY	Exercise	Time	Distance/ resistance	Intensity	Heart rate	Ease	Cal/kJ expended
							Total:

THURSDAY	Exercise	Time	Distance/ resistance	Intensity	Heart rate	Ease	Cal/kJ expended
							Total:

FRIDAY	Exercise	Time	Distance/ resistance	Intensity	Heart rate	Ease	Cal/kJ expended
							Total:

SATURDAY	Exercise	Time	Distance/ resistance	Intensity	Heart rate	Ease	Cal/kJ expended
							Total:

SUNDAY	Exercise	Time	Distance/ resistance	Intensity	Heart rate	Ease	Cal/kJ expended
							Total:
							Weekly Total:

Food Diary

MONDAY		Cal/kJ	Fat	Protein	Carbs
Breakfast time: am/pm					
Lunch time: am/pm					
Dinner time: am/pm					
Snacks:					
Coffees/teas:	Fluid intake: **Totals:**				

TUESDAY		Cal/kJ	Fat	Protein	Carbs
Breakfast time: am/pm					
Lunch time: am/pm					
Dinner time: am/pm					
Snacks:					
Coffees/teas:	Fluid intake: **Totals:**				

WEDNESDAY		Cal/kJ	Fat	Protein	Carbs
Breakfast time: am/pm					
Lunch time: am/pm					
Dinner time: am/pm					
Snacks:					
Coffees/teas:	Fluid intake: **Totals:**				

THURSDAY		Cal/kJ	Fat	Protein	Carbs
Breakfast time: am/pm					
Lunch time: am/pm					
Dinner time: am/pm					
Snacks:					
Coffees/teas:	Fluid intake: **Totals:**				

FRIDAY		Cal/kJ	Fat	Protein	Carbs
Breakfast time: am/pm					
Lunch time: am/pm					
Dinner time: am/pm					
Snacks:					
Coffees/teas:	Fluid intake: **Totals:**				

SATURDAY		Cal/kJ	Fat	Protein	Carbs
Breakfast time: am/pm					
Lunch time: am/pm					
Dinner time: am/pm					
Snacks:					
Coffees/teas:	Fluid intake: **Totals:**				

SUNDAY		Cal/kJ	Fat	Protein	Carbs
Breakfast time: am/pm					
Lunch time: am/pm					
Dinner time: am/pm					
Snacks:					
Coffees/teas:	Fluid intake: **Totals:**				

Units of alcohol this week: ______ Total alcohol Cal/kJ: ______

Vitamins and supplements

Weekly Totals	Cal/kJ	Fat	Protein	Carbs

Weekly Personal Summary

Energy level (1–5) ______ Stress level (1–5) ______

Hours of sleep ______ Sleep quality (1–5) ______

Mood (1–5) ______ Appetite (1–5) ______

Cal/kJ intake

Planned Cal/kJ	
Actual Cal/kJ	

Difference [+/-] ______

Weight at start of week ______

Weight at end of week ______

BMI at start of week ______

BMI at end of week ______

Injuries or illnesses ______

Week Beginning

/ /

Planned exercise sessions this week

	Exercise	Completed [Y/N]
Monday		
Tuesday		
Wednesday		
Thursday		
Friday		
Saturday		
Sunday		

Strength Training

	Focus area	Equipment	SET 1		SET 2		SET 3		SET 4	
MONDAY			Weight	Reps	Weight	Reps	Weight	Reps	Weight	Reps

	Focus area	Equipment	SET 1		SET 2		SET 3		SET 4	
TUESDAY			Weight	Reps	Weight	Reps	Weight	Reps	Weight	Reps

	Focus area	Equipment	SET 1		SET 2		SET 3		SET 4	
WEDNESDAY			Weight	Reps	Weight	Reps	Weight	Reps	Weight	Reps

	Focus area	Equipment	SET 1		SET 2		SET 3		SET 4	
THURSDAY			Weight	Reps	Weight	Reps	Weight	Reps	Weight	Reps

	Focus area	Equipment	SET 1		SET 2		SET 3		SET 4	
FRIDAY			Weight	Reps	Weight	Reps	Weight	Reps	Weight	Reps

	Focus area	Equipment	SET 1		SET 2		SET 3		SET 4	
SATURDAY			Weight	Reps	Weight	Reps	Weight	Reps	Weight	Reps

	Focus area	Equipment	SET 1		SET 2		SET 3		SET 4	
SUNDAY			Weight	Reps	Weight	Reps	Weight	Reps	Weight	Reps

Cardio Training

MONDAY

Exercise	Time	Distance/ resistance	Intensity	Heart rate	Ease	Cal/kJ expended
						Total:

TUESDAY

Exercise	Time	Distance/ resistance	Intensity	Heart rate	Ease	Cal/kJ expended
						Total:

WEDNESDAY

Exercise	Time	Distance/ resistance	Intensity	Heart rate	Ease	Cal/kJ expended
						Total:

THURSDAY

Exercise	Time	Distance/ resistance	Intensity	Heart rate	Ease	Cal/kJ expended
						Total:

FRIDAY

Exercise	Time	Distance/ resistance	Intensity	Heart rate	Ease	Cal/kJ expended
						Total:

SATURDAY

Exercise	Time	Distance/ resistance	Intensity	Heart rate	Ease	Cal/kJ expended
						Total:

SUNDAY

Exercise	Time	Distance/ resistance	Intensity	Heart rate	Ease	Cal/kJ expended
						Total:
					Weekly Total:	

Food Diary

MONDAY		Cal/kJ	Fat	Protein	Carbs
Breakfast time: am/pm					
Lunch time: am/pm					
Dinner time: am/pm					
Snacks:					
Coffees/teas:	Fluid intake: **Totals:**				

TUESDAY		Cal/kJ	Fat	Protein	Carbs
Breakfast time: am/pm					
Lunch time: am/pm					
Dinner time: am/pm					
Snacks:					
Coffees/teas:	Fluid intake: **Totals:**				

WEDNESDAY		Cal/kJ	Fat	Protein	Carbs
Breakfast time: am/pm					
Lunch time: am/pm					
Dinner time: am/pm					
Snacks:					
Coffees/teas:	Fluid intake: **Totals:**				

THURSDAY		Cal/kJ	Fat	Protein	Carbs
Breakfast time: am/pm					
Lunch time: am/pm					
Dinner time: am/pm					
Snacks:					
Coffees/teas:	Fluid intake: **Totals:**				

FRIDAY			Cal/kJ	Fat	Protein	Carbs
Breakfast time: am/pm						
Lunch time: am/pm						
Dinner time: am/pm						
Snacks:						
Coffees/teas:	Fluid intake:	**Totals:**				

SATURDAY			Cal/kJ	Fat	Protein	Carbs
Breakfast time: am/pm						
Lunch time: am/pm						
Dinner time: am/pm						
Snacks:						
Coffees/teas:	Fluid intake:	**Totals:**				

SUNDAY			Cal/kJ	Fat	Protein	Carbs
Breakfast time: am/pm						
Lunch time: am/pm						
Dinner time: am/pm						
Snacks:						
Coffees/teas:	Fluid intake:	**Totals:**				

Units of alcohol this week: ____ Total alcohol Cal/kJ: ____

Vitamins and supplements

Weekly Totals	Cal/kJ	Fat	Protein	Carbs

Weekly Personal Summary

Energy level (1–5) ____ Stress level (1–5) ____

Hours of sleep ____ Sleep quality (1–5) ____

Mood (1–5) ____ Appetite (1–5) ____

Cal/kJ intake

Planned Cal/kJ	
Actual Cal/kJ	
Difference [+/-]	

Weight at start of week ____

Weight at end of week ____

BMI at start of week ____

BMI at end of week ____

Injuries or illnesses ____

Week Beginning

/ /

Planned exercise sessions this week

	Exercise	Completed [Y/N]
Monday		
Tuesday		
Wednesday		
Thursday		
Friday		
Saturday		
Sunday		

Strength Training

MONDAY	ocus area	Equipment	SET 1		SET 2		SET 3		SET 4	
			Weight	Reps	Weight	Reps	Weight	Reps	Weight	Reps

TUESDAY	ocus area	Equipment	SET 1		SET 2		SET 3		SET 4	
			Weight	Reps	Weight	Reps	Weight	Reps	Weight	Reps

WEDNESDAY	ocus area	Equipment	SET 1		SET 2		SET 3		SET 4	
			Weight	Reps	Weight	Reps	Weight	Reps	Weight	Reps

THURSDAY	ocus area	Equipment	SET 1		SET 2		SET 3		SET 4	
			Weight	Reps	Weight	Reps	Weight	Reps	Weight	Reps

FRIDAY	ocus area	Equipment	SET 1		SET 2		SET 3		SET 4	
			Weight	Reps	Weight	Reps	Weight	Reps	Weight	Reps

SATURDAY	ocus area	Equipment	SET 1		SET 2		SET 3		SET 4	
			Weight	Reps	Weight	Reps	Weight	Reps	Weight	Reps

SUNDAY	ocus area	Equipment	SET 1		SET 2		SET 3		SET 4	
			Weight	Reps	Weight	Reps	Weight	Reps	Weight	Reps

Cardio Training

MONDAY

Exercise	Time	Distance/ resistance	Intensity	Heart rate	Ease	Cal/kJ expended
						Total:

TUESDAY

Exercise	Time	Distance/ resistance	Intensity	Heart rate	Ease	Cal/kJ expended
						Total:

WEDNESDAY

Exercise	Time	Distance/ resistance	Intensity	Heart rate	Ease	Cal/kJ expended
						Total:

THURSDAY

Exercise	Time	Distance/ resistance	Intensity	Heart rate	Ease	Cal/kJ expended
						Total:

FRIDAY

Exercise	Time	Distance/ resistance	Intensity	Heart rate	Ease	Cal/kJ expended
						Total:

SATURDAY

Exercise	Time	Distance/ resistance	Intensity	Heart rate	Ease	Cal/kJ expended
						Total:

SUNDAY

Exercise	Time	Distance/ resistance	Intensity	Heart rate	Ease	Cal/kJ expended
						Total:

Weekly Total:

Food Diary

MONDAY				Cal/kJ	Fat	Protein	Carbs
Breakfast time: am/pm							
Lunch time: am/pm							
Dinner time: am/pm							
Snacks:							
Coffees/teas:	Fluid intake:		**Totals:**				

TUESDAY				Cal/kJ	Fat	Protein	Carbs
Breakfast time: am/pm							
Lunch time: am/pm							
Dinner time: am/pm							
Snacks:							
Coffees/teas:	Fluid intake:		**Totals:**				

WEDNESDAY				Cal/kJ	Fat	Protein	Carbs
Breakfast time: am/pm							
Lunch time: am/pm							
Dinner time: am/pm							
Snacks:							
Coffees/teas:	Fluid intake:		**Totals:**				

THURSDAY				Cal/kJ	Fat	Protein	Carbs
Breakfast time: am/pm							
Lunch time: am/pm							
Dinner time: am/pm							
Snacks:							
Coffees/teas:	Fluid intake:		**Totals:**				

FRIDAY		Cal/kJ	Fat	Protein	Carbs
Breakfast time: am/pm					
Lunch time: am/pm					
Dinner time: am/pm					
Snacks:					
Coffees/teas:	Fluid intake: **Totals:**				

SATURDAY		Cal/kJ	Fat	Protein	Carbs
Breakfast time: am/pm					
Lunch time: am/pm					
Dinner time: am/pm					
Snacks:					
Coffees/teas:	Fluid intake: **Totals:**				

SUNDAY		Cal/kJ	Fat	Protein	Carbs
Breakfast time: am/pm					
Lunch time: am/pm					
Dinner time: am/pm					
Snacks:					
Coffees/teas:	Fluid intake: **Totals:**				

Units of alcohol this week: Total alcohol Cal/kJ:

Vitamins and supplements

Weekly Totals	Cal/kJ	Fat	Protein	Carbs

Weekly Personal Summary

Energy level 1–5 Stress level 1–5

Hours of sleep Sleep quality 1–5

Mood 1–5 Appetite 1–5

Cal/kJ intake

Planned Cal/kJ	
Actual Cal/kJ	

Difference [+/-]

Weight at start of week

Weight at end of week

BMI at start of week

BMI at end of week

Injuries or illnesses

Week Beginning

/ /

Planned exercise sessions this week

	Exercise	Completed [Y/N]
Monday		
Tuesday		
Wednesday		
Thursday		
Friday		
Saturday		
Sunday		

Strength Training

MONDAY

ocus area	Equipment	SET 1		SET 2		SET 3		SET 4	
		Weight	Reps	Weight	Reps	Weight	Reps	Weight	Reps

TUESDAY

ocus area	Equipment	SET 1		SET 2		SET 3		SET 4	
		Weight	Reps	Weight	Reps	Weight	Reps	Weight	Reps

WEDNESDAY

ocus area	Equipment	SET 1		SET 2		SET 3		SET 4	
		Weight	Reps	Weight	Reps	Weight	Reps	Weight	Reps

THURSDAY

ocus area	Equipment	SET 1		SET 2		SET 3		SET 4	
		Weight	Reps	Weight	Reps	Weight	Reps	Weight	Reps

FRIDAY

Focus area	Equipment	SET 1		SET 2		SET 3		SET 4	
		Weight	Reps	Weight	Reps	Weight	Reps	Weight	Reps

SATURDAY

ocus area	Equipment	SET 1		SET 2		SET 3		SET 4	
		Weight	Reps	Weight	Reps	Weight	Reps	Weight	Reps

SUNDAY

ocus area	Equipment	SET 1		SET 2		SET 3		SET 4	
		Weight	Reps	Weight	Reps	Weight	Reps	Weight	Reps

Cardio Training

MONDAY	Exercise	Time	Distance/ resistance	Intensity	Heart rate	Ease	Cal/kJ expended
							Total:

TUESDAY	Exercise	Time	Distance/ resistance	Intensity	Heart rate	Ease	Cal/kJ expended
							Total:

WEDNESDAY	Exercise	Time	Distance/ resistance	Intensity	Heart rate	Ease	Cal/kJ expended
							Total:

THURSDAY	Exercise	Time	Distance/ resistance	Intensity	Heart rate	Ease	Cal/kJ expended
							Total:

FRIDAY	Exercise	Time	Distance/ resistance	Intensity	Heart rate	Ease	Cal/kJ expended
							Total:

SATURDAY	Exercise	Time	Distance/ resistance	Intensity	Heart rate	Ease	Cal/kJ expended
							Total:

SUNDAY	Exercise	Time	Distance/ resistance	Intensity	Heart rate	Ease	Cal/kJ expended
							Total:
							Weekly Total:

Food Diary

MONDAY		Cal/kJ	Fat	Protein	Carbs
Breakfast time: am/pm					
Lunch time: am/pm					
Dinner time: am/pm					
Snacks:					
Coffees/teas:	Fluid intake: **Totals:**				

TUESDAY		Cal/kJ	Fat	Protein	Carbs
Breakfast time: am/pm					
Lunch time: am/pm					
Dinner time: am/pm					
Snacks:					
Coffees/teas:	Fluid intake: **Totals:**				

WEDNESDAY		Cal/kJ	Fat	Protein	Carbs
Breakfast time: am/pm					
Lunch time: am/pm					
Dinner time: am/pm					
Snacks:					
Coffees/teas:	Fluid intake: **Totals:**				

THURSDAY		Cal/kJ	Fat	Protein	Carbs
Breakfast time: am/pm					
Lunch time: am/pm					
Dinner time: am/pm					
Snacks:					
Coffees/teas:	Fluid intake: **Totals:**				

FRIDAY		Cal/kJ	Fat	Protein	Carbs
Breakfast time: am/pm					
Lunch time: am/pm					
Dinner time: am/pm					
Snacks:					
Coffees/teas:	Fluid intake: **Totals:**				

SATURDAY		Cal/kJ	Fat	Protein	Carbs
Breakfast time: am/pm					
Lunch time: am/pm					
Dinner time: am/pm					
Snacks:					
Coffees/teas:	Fluid intake: **Totals:**				

SUNDAY		Cal/kJ	Fat	Protein	Carbs
Breakfast time: am/pm					
Lunch time: am/pm					
Dinner time: am/pm					
Snacks:					
Coffees/teas:	Fluid intake: **Totals:**				

Units of alcohol this week: Total alcohol Cal/kJ:

Vitamins and supplements

Weekly Totals	Cal/kJ	Fat	Protein	Carbs

Weekly Personal Summary

Energy level 1–5 Stress level 1–5

Hours of sleep Sleep quality 1–5

Mood 1–5 Appetite 1–5

Cal/kJ intake

Planned Cal/kJ

Actual Cal/kJ

Difference [+/-]

Weight at start of week

Weight at end of week

BMI at start of week

BMI at end of week

Injuries or illnesses

Week Beginning

/ /

Strength Training

Planned exercise sessions this week

	Exercise	Completed [Y/N]
Monday		
Tuesday		
Wednesday		
Thursday		
Friday		
Saturday		
Sunday		

MONDAY	ocus area	Equipment	SET 1		SET 2		SET 3		SET 4	
			Weight	Reps	Weight	Reps	Weight	Reps	Weight	Reps

TUESDAY	Focus area	Equipment	SET 1		SET 2		SET 3		SET 4	
			Weight	Reps	Weight	Reps	Weight	Reps	Weight	Reps

WEDNESDAY	ocus area	Equipment	SET 1		SET 2		SET 3		SET 4	
			Weight	Reps	Weight	Reps	Weight	Reps	Weight	Reps

THURSDAY	ocus area	Equipment	SET 1		SET 2		SET 3		SET 4	
			Weight	Reps	Weight	Reps	Weight	Reps	Weight	Reps

FRIDAY	Focus area	Equipment	SET 1		SET 2		SET 3		SET 4	
			Weight	Reps	Weight	Reps	Weight	Reps	Weight	Reps

SATURDAY	ocus area	Equipment	SET 1		SET 2		SET 3		SET 4	
			Weight	Reps	Weight	Reps	Weight	Reps	Weight	Reps

SUNDAY	Focus area	Equipment	SET 1		SET 2		SET 3		SET 4	
			Weight	Reps	Weight	Reps	Weight	Reps	Weight	Reps

Cardio Training

MONDAY	Exercise	Time	Distance/ resistance	Intensity	Heart rate	Ease	Cal/kJ expended
							Total:

TUESDAY	Exercise	Time	Distance/ resistance	Intensity	Heart rate	Ease	Cal/kJ expended
							Total:

WEDNESDAY	Exercise	Time	Distance/ resistance	Intensity	Heart rate	Ease	Cal/kJ expended
							Total:

THURSDAY	Exercise	Time	Distance/ resistance	Intensity	Heart rate	Ease	Cal/kJ expended
							Total:

FRIDAY	Exercise	Time	Distance/ resistance	Intensity	Heart rate	Ease	Cal/kJ expended
							Total:

SATURDAY	Exercise	Time	Distance/ resistance	Intensity	Heart rate	Ease	Cal/kJ expended
							Total:

SUNDAY	Exercise	Time	Distance/ resistance	Intensity	Heart rate	Ease	Cal/kJ expended
							Total:
							Weekly Total:

Food Diary

MONDAY		Cal/kJ	Fat	Protein	Carbs
Breakfast time: am/pm					
Lunch time: am/pm					
Dinner time: am/pm					
Snacks:					
Coffees/teas:	Fluid intake: **Totals:**				

TUESDAY		Cal/kJ	Fat	Protein	Carbs
Breakfast time: am/pm					
Lunch time: am/pm					
Dinner time: am/pm					
Snacks:					
Coffees/teas:	Fluid intake: **Totals:**				

WEDNESDAY		Cal/kJ	Fat	Protein	Carbs
Breakfast time: am/pm					
Lunch time: am/pm					
Dinner time: am/pm					
Snacks:					
Coffees/teas:	Fluid intake: **Totals:**				

THURSDAY		Cal/kJ	Fat	Protein	Carbs
Breakfast time: am/pm					
Lunch time: am/pm					
Dinner time: am/pm					
Snacks:					
Coffees/teas:	Fluid intake: **Totals:**				

FRIDAY		Cal/kJ	Fat	Protein	Carbs
Breakfast time: am/pm					
Lunch time: am/pm					
Dinner time: am/pm					
Snacks:					
Coffees/teas:	Fluid intake: **Totals:**				

SATURDAY		Cal/kJ	Fat	Protein	Carbs
Breakfast time: am/pm					
Lunch time: am/pm					
Dinner time: am/pm					
Snacks:					
Coffees/teas:	Fluid intake: **Totals:**				

SUNDAY		Cal/kJ	Fat	Protein	Carbs
Breakfast time: am/pm					
Lunch time: am/pm					
Dinner time: am/pm					
Snacks:					
Coffees/teas:	Fluid intake: **Totals:**				

Units of alcohol this week: Total alcohol Cal/kJ:

Vitamins and supplements

Weekly Totals	Cal/kJ	Fat	Protein	Carbs

Weekly Personal Summary

Energy level (1–5)

Stress level (1–5)

Hours of sleep

Sleep quality (1–5)

Mood (1–5)

Appetite (1–5)

Cal/kJ intake

Planned Cal/kJ

Actual Cal/kJ

Difference [+/-]

Weight at start of week

Weight at end of week

BMI at start of week

BMI at end of week

Injuries or illnesses

Week Beginning

/ /

Planned exercise sessions this week

	Exercise	Completed [Y/N]
Monday		
Tuesday		
Wednesday		
Thursday		
Friday		
Saturday		
Sunday		

Strength Training

MONDAY

ocus area	Equipment	SET 1		SET 2		SET 3		SET 4	
		Weight	Reps	Weight	Reps	Weight	Reps	Weight	Reps

TUESDAY

ocus area	Equipment	SET 1		SET 2		SET 3		SET 4	
		Weight	Reps	Weight	Reps	Weight	Reps	Weight	Reps

WEDNESDAY

ocus area	Equipment	SET 1		SET 2		SET 3		SET 4	
		Weight	Reps	Weight	Reps	Weight	Reps	Weight	Reps

THURSDAY

ocus area	Equipment	SET 1		SET 2		SET 3		SET 4	
		Weight	Reps	Weight	Reps	Weight	Reps	Weight	Reps

FRIDAY

ocus area	Equipment	SET 1		SET 2		SET 3		SET 4	
		Weight	Reps	Weight	Reps	Weight	Reps	Weight	Reps

SATURDAY

ocus area	Equipment	SET 1		SET 2		SET 3		SET 4	
		Weight	Reps	Weight	Reps	Weight	Reps	Weight	Reps

SUNDAY

ocus area	Equipment	SET 1		SET 2		SET 3		SET 4	
		Weight	Reps	Weight	Reps	Weight	Reps	Weight	Reps

Cardio Training

MONDAY

Exercise	Time	Distance/ resistance	Intensity	Heart rate	Ease	Cal/kJ expended
						Total:

TUESDAY

Exercise	Time	Distance/ resistance	Intensity	Heart rate	Ease	Cal/kJ expended
						Total:

WEDNESDAY

Exercise	Time	Distance/ resistance	Intensity	Heart rate	Ease	Cal/kJ expended
						Total:

THURSDAY

Exercise	Time	Distance/ resistance	Intensity	Heart rate	Ease	Cal/kJ expended
						Total:

FRIDAY

Exercise	Time	Distance/ resistance	Intensity	Heart rate	Ease	Cal/kJ expended
						Total:

SATURDAY

Exercise	Time	Distance/ resistance	Intensity	Heart rate	Ease	Cal/kJ expended
						Total:

SUNDAY

Exercise	Time	Distance/ resistance	Intensity	Heart rate	Ease	Cal/kJ expended
						Total:
						Weekly Total:

Food Diary

MONDAY		Cal/kJ	Fat	Protein	Carbs
Breakfast time: am/pm					
Lunch time: am/pm					
Dinner time: am/pm					
Snacks:					
Coffees/teas:	Fluid intake: **Totals:**				

TUESDAY		Cal/kJ	Fat	Protein	Carbs
Breakfast time: am/pm					
Lunch time: am/pm					
Dinner time: am/pm					
Snacks:					
Coffees/teas:	Fluid intake: **Totals:**				

WEDNESDAY		Cal/kJ	Fat	Protein	Carbs
Breakfast time: am/pm					
Lunch time: am/pm					
Dinner time: am/pm					
Snacks:					
Coffees/teas:	Fluid intake: **Totals:**				

THURSDAY		Cal/kJ	Fat	Protein	Carbs
Breakfast time: am/pm					
Lunch time: am/pm					
Dinner time: am/pm					
Snacks:					
Coffees/teas:	Fluid intake: **Totals:**				

FRIDAY		Cal/kJ	Fat	Protein	Carbs
Breakfast time: am/pm					
Lunch time: am/pm					
Dinner time: am/pm					
Snacks:					
Coffees/teas:	Fluid intake: **Totals:**				

SATURDAY		Cal/kJ	Fat	Protein	Carbs
Breakfast time: am/pm					
Lunch time: am/pm					
Dinner time: am/pm					
Snacks:					
Coffees/teas:	Fluid intake: **Totals:**				

SUNDAY		Cal/kJ	Fat	Protein	Carbs
Breakfast time: am/pm					
Lunch time: am/pm					
Dinner time: am/pm					
Snacks:					
Coffees/teas:	Fluid intake: **Totals:**				

Units of alcohol this week: Total alcohol Cal/kJ:

Vitamins and supplements

Weekly Totals	Cal/kJ	Fat	Protein	Carbs

Weekly Personal Summary

Energy level (1–5)

Stress level (1–5)

Hours of sleep

Sleep quality (1–5)

Mood (1–5)

Appetite (1–5)

Cal/kJ intake

Planned Cal/kJ	
Actual Cal/kJ	

Difference [+/-]

Weight at start of week

Weight at end of week

BMI at start of week

BMI at end of week

Injuries or illnesses

Week Beginning

/ /

Planned exercise sessions this week

	Exercise	Completed [Y/N]
Monday		
Tuesday		
Wednesday		
Thursday		
Friday		
Saturday		
Sunday		

Strength Training

	ocus area	Equipment	SET 1		SET 2		SET 3		SET 4	
			Weight	Reps	Weight	Reps	Weight	Reps	Weight	Reps
MONDAY										

	ocus area	Equipment	SET 1		SET 2		SET 3		SET 4	
			Weight	Reps	Weight	Reps	Weight	Reps	Weight	Reps
TUESDAY										

	ocus area	Equipment	SET 1		SET 2		SET 3		SET 4	
			Weight	Reps	Weight	Reps	Weight	Reps	Weight	Reps
WEDNESDAY										

	ocus area	Equipment	SET 1		SET 2		SET 3		SET 4	
			Weight	Reps	Weight	Reps	Weight	Reps	Weight	Reps
THURSDAY										

	ocus area	Equipment	SET 1		SET 2		SET 3		SET 4	
			Weight	Reps	Weight	Reps	Weight	Reps	Weight	Reps
FRIDAY										

	ocus area	Equipment	SET 1		SET 2		SET 3		SET 4	
			Weight	Reps	Weight	Reps	Weight	Reps	Weight	Reps
SATURDAY										

	ocus area	Equipment	SET 1		SET 2		SET 3		SET 4	
			Weight	Reps	Weight	Reps	Weight	Reps	Weight	Reps
SUNDAY										

Cardio Training

MONDAY

Exercise	Time	Distance/ resistance	Intensity	Heart rate	Ease	Cal/kJ expended
						Total:

TUESDAY

Exercise	Time	Distance/ resistance	Intensity	Heart rate	Ease	Cal/kJ expended
						Total:

WEDNESDAY

Exercise	Time	Distance/ resistance	Intensity	Heart rate	Ease	Cal/kJ expended
						Total:

THURSDAY

Exercise	Time	Distance/ resistance	Intensity	Heart rate	Ease	Cal/kJ expended
						Total:

FRIDAY

Exercise	Time	Distance/ resistance	Intensity	Heart rate	Ease	Cal/kJ expended
						Total:

SATURDAY

Exercise	Time	Distance/ resistance	Intensity	Heart rate	Ease	Cal/kJ expended
						Total:

SUNDAY

Exercise	Time	Distance/ resistance	Intensity	Heart rate	Ease	Cal/kJ expended
						Total:
						Weekly Total:

Food Diary

MONDAY		Cal/kJ	Fat	Protein	Carbs
Breakfast time: am/pm					
Lunch time: am/pm					
Dinner time: am/pm					
Snacks:					
Coffees/teas:	Fluid intake: **Totals:**				

TUESDAY		Cal/kJ	Fat	Protein	Carbs
Breakfast time: am/pm					
Lunch time: am/pm					
Dinner time: am/pm					
Snacks:					
Coffees/teas:	Fluid intake: **Totals:**				

WEDNESDAY		Cal/kJ	Fat	Protein	Carbs
Breakfast time: am/pm					
Lunch time: am/pm					
Dinner time: am/pm					
Snacks:					
Coffees/teas:	Fluid intake: **Totals:**				

THURSDAY		Cal/kJ	Fat	Protein	Carbs
Breakfast time: am/pm					
Lunch time: am/pm					
Dinner time: am/pm					
Snacks:					
Coffees/teas:	Fluid intake: **Totals:**				

FRIDAY		Cal/kJ	Fat	Protein	Carbs
Breakfast time: am/pm					
Lunch time: am/pm					
Dinner time: am/pm					
Snacks:					
Coffees/teas:	Fluid intake: **Totals:**				

SATURDAY		Cal/kJ	Fat	Protein	Carbs
Breakfast time: am/pm					
Lunch time: am/pm					
Dinner time: am/pm					
Snacks:					
Coffees/teas:	Fluid intake: **Totals:**				

SUNDAY		Cal/kJ	Fat	Protein	Carbs
Breakfast time: am/pm					
Lunch time: am/pm					
Dinner time: am/pm					
Snacks:					
Coffees/teas:	Fluid intake: **Totals:**				

Units of alcohol this week: Total alcohol Cal/kJ:

Vitamins and supplements

Weekly Totals	Cal/kJ	Fat	Protein	Carbs

Weekly Personal Summary

Energy level (1–5) Stress level (1–5)

Hours of sleep Sleep quality (1–5)

Mood (1–5) Appetite (1–5)

Cal/kJ intake

Planned Cal/kJ	
Actual Cal/kJ	
Difference [+/-]	

Weight at start of week

Weight at end of week

BMI at start of week

BMI at end of week

Injuries or illnesses

Week Beginning

/ /

Strength Training

Planned exercise sessions this week

	Exercise	Completed [Y/N]
Monday		
Tuesday		
Wednesday		
Thursday		
Friday		
Saturday		
Sunday		

MONDAY	ocus area	Equipment	SET 1		SET 2		SET 3		SET 4	
			Weight	Reps	Weight	Reps	Weight	Reps	Weight	Reps

TUESDAY	ocus area	Equipment	SET 1		SET 2		SET 3		SET 4	
			Weight	Reps	Weight	Reps	Weight	Reps	Weight	Reps

WEDNESDAY	ocus area	Equipment	SET 1		SET 2		SET 3		SET 4	
			Weight	Reps	Weight	Reps	Weight	Reps	Weight	Reps

THURSDAY	ocus area	Equipment	SET 1		SET 2		SET 3		SET 4	
			Weight	Reps	Weight	Reps	Weight	Reps	Weight	Reps

FRIDAY	ocus area	Equipment	SET 1		SET 2		SET 3		SET 4	
			Weight	Reps	Weight	Reps	Weight	Reps	Weight	Reps

SATURDAY	Focus area	Equipment	SET 1		SET 2		SET 3		SET 4	
			Weight	Reps	Weight	Reps	Weight	Reps	Weight	Reps

SUNDAY	Focus area	Equipment	SET 1		SET 2		SET 3		SET 4	
			Weight	Reps	Weight	Reps	Weight	Reps	Weight	Reps

Cardio Training

MONDAY

Exercise	Time	Distance/ resistance	Intensity	Heart rate	Ease	Cal/kJ expended
						Total:

TUESDAY

Exercise	Time	Distance/ resistance	Intensity	Heart rate	Ease	Cal/kJ expended
						Total:

WEDNESDAY

Exercise	Time	Distance/ resistance	Intensity	Heart rate	Ease	Cal/kJ expended
						Total:

THURSDAY

Exercise	Time	Distance/ resistance	Intensity	Heart rate	Ease	Cal/kJ expended
						Total:

FRIDAY

Exercise	Time	Distance/ resistance	Intensity	Heart rate	Ease	Cal/kJ expended
						Total:

SATURDAY

Exercise	Time	Distance/ resistance	Intensity	Heart rate	Ease	Cal/kJ expended
						Total:

SUNDAY

Exercise	Time	Distance/ resistance	Intensity	Heart rate	Ease	Cal/kJ expended
						Total:
						Weekly Total:

Food Diary

MONDAY		Cal/kJ	Fat	Protein	Carbs
Breakfast time: am/pm					
Lunch time: am/pm					
Dinner time: am/pm					
Snacks:					
Coffees/teas:	Fluid intake: **Totals:**				

TUESDAY		Cal/kJ	Fat	Protein	Carbs
Breakfast time: am/pm					
Lunch time: am/pm					
Dinner time: am/pm					
Snacks:					
Coffees/teas:	Fluid intake: **Totals:**				

WEDNESDAY		Cal/kJ	Fat	Protein	Carbs
Breakfast time: am/pm					
Lunch time: am/pm					
Dinner time: am/pm					
Snacks:					
Coffees/teas:	Fluid intake: **Totals:**				

THURSDAY		Cal/kJ	Fat	Protein	Carbs
Breakfast time: am/pm					
Lunch time: am/pm					
Dinner time: am/pm					
Snacks:					
Coffees/teas:	Fluid intake: **Totals:**				

FRIDAY		Cal/kJ	Fat	Protein	Carbs
Breakfast time: am/pm					
Lunch time: am/pm					
Dinner time: am/pm					
Snacks:					
Coffees/teas:	Fluid intake: **Totals:**				

SATURDAY		Cal/kJ	Fat	Protein	Carbs
Breakfast time: am/pm					
Lunch time: am/pm					
Dinner time: am/pm					
Snacks:					
Coffees/teas:	Fluid intake: **Totals:**				

SUNDAY		Cal/kJ	Fat	Protein	Carbs
Breakfast time: am/pm					
Lunch time: am/pm					
Dinner time: am/pm					
Snacks:					
Coffees/teas:	Fluid intake: **Totals:**				

Units of alcohol this week: Total alcohol Cal/kJ:

Vitamins and supplements

Weekly Totals	Cal/kJ	Fat	Protein	Carbs

Weekly Personal Summary

Energy level (1–5)
Stress level (1–5)
Hours of sleep
Sleep quality (1–5)
Mood (1–5)
Appetite (1–5)

Cal/kJ intake

Planned Cal/kJ	
Actual Cal/kJ	

Difference [+/-]

Weight at start of week
Weight at end of week
BMI at start of week
BMI at end of week

Injuries or illnesses

Week Beginning

/ /

Planned exercise sessions this week

	Exercise	Completed [Y/N]
Monday		
Tuesday		
Wednesday		
Thursday		
Friday		
Saturday		
Sunday		

Strength Training

MONDAY	ocus area	Equipment	SET 1		SET 2		SET 3		SET 4	
			Weight	Reps	Weight	Reps	Weight	Reps	Weight	Reps

TUESDAY	ocus area	Equipment	SET 1		SET 2		SET 3		SET 4	
			Weight	Reps	Weight	Reps	Weight	Reps	Weight	Reps

WEDNESDAY	ocus area	Equipment	SET 1		SET 2		SET 3		SET 4	
			Weight	Reps	Weight	Reps	Weight	Reps	Weight	Reps

THURSDAY	ocus area	Equipment	SET 1		SET 2		SET 3		SET 4	
			Weight	Reps	Weight	Reps	Weight	Reps	Weight	Reps

FRIDAY	ocus area	Equipment	SET 1		SET 2		SET 3		SET 4	
			Weight	Reps	Weight	Reps	Weight	Reps	Weight	Reps

SATURDAY	ocus area	Equipment	SET 1		SET 2		SET 3		SET 4	
			Weight	Reps	Weight	Reps	Weight	Reps	Weight	Reps

SUNDAY	ocus area	Equipment	SET 1		SET 2		SET 3		SET 4	
			Weight	Reps	Weight	Reps	Weight	Reps	Weight	Reps

Cardio Training

MONDAY

Exercise	Time	Distance/ resistance	Intensity	Heart rate	Ease	Cal/kJ expended
						Total:

TUESDAY

Exercise	Time	Distance/ resistance	Intensity	Heart rate	Ease	Cal/kJ expended
						Total:

WEDNESDAY

Exercise	Time	Distance/ resistance	Intensity	Heart rate	Ease	Cal/kJ expended
						Total:

THURSDAY

Exercise	Time	Distance/ resistance	Intensity	Heart rate	Ease	Cal/kJ expended
						Total:

FRIDAY

Exercise	Time	Distance/ resistance	Intensity	Heart rate	Ease	Cal/kJ expended
						Total:

SATURDAY

Exercise	Time	Distance/ resistance	Intensity	Heart rate	Ease	Cal/kJ expended
						Total:

SUNDAY

Exercise	Time	Distance/ resistance	Intensity	Heart rate	Ease	Cal/kJ expended
						Total:
						Weekly Total:

Food Diary

MONDAY		Cal/kJ	Fat	Protein	Carbs
Breakfast time: am/pm					
Lunch time: am/pm					
Dinner time: am/pm					
Snacks:					
Coffees/teas:	Fluid intake: **Totals:**				

TUESDAY		Cal/kJ	Fat	Protein	Carbs
Breakfast time: am/pm					
Lunch time: am/pm					
Dinner time: am/pm					
Snacks:					
Coffees/teas:	Fluid intake: **Totals:**				

WEDNESDAY		Cal/kJ	Fat	Protein	Carbs
Breakfast time: am/pm					
Lunch time: am/pm					
Dinner time: am/pm					
Snacks:					
Coffees/teas:	Fluid intake: **Totals:**				

THURSDAY		Cal/kJ	Fat	Protein	Carbs
Breakfast time: am/pm					
Lunch time: am/pm					
Dinner time: am/pm					
Snacks:					
Coffees/teas:	Fluid intake: **Totals:**				

FRIDAY		Cal/kJ	Fat	Protein	Carbs
Breakfast time: am/pm					
Lunch time: am/pm					
Dinner time: am/pm					
Snacks:					
Coffees/teas:	Fluid intake: **Totals:**				

SATURDAY		Cal/kJ	Fat	Protein	Carbs
Breakfast time: am/pm					
Lunch time: am/pm					
Dinner time: am/pm					
Snacks:					
Coffees/teas:	Fluid intake: **Totals:**				

SUNDAY		Cal/kJ	Fat	Protein	Carbs
Breakfast time: am/pm					
Lunch time: am/pm					
Dinner time: am/pm					
Snacks:					
Coffees/teas:	Fluid intake: **Totals:**				

Units of alcohol this week: Total alcohol Cal/kJ:

Vitamins and supplements

Weekly Totals	Cal/kJ	Fat	Protein	Carbs

Weekly Personal Summary

Energy level (1–5) Stress level (1–5)

Hours of sleep Sleep quality (1–5)

Mood (1–5) Appetite (1–5)

Cal/kJ intake

Planned Cal/kJ

Actual Cal/kJ

Difference [+/-]

Weight at start of week

Weight at end of week

BMI at start of week

BMI at end of week

Injuries or illnesses

Week Beginning

/ /

Planned exercise sessions this week

	Exercise	Completed [Y/N]
Monday		
Tuesday		
Wednesday		
Thursday		
Friday		
Saturday		
Sunday		

Strength Training

MONDAY

Focus area	Equipment	SET 1		SET 2		SET 3		SET 4	
		Weight	Reps	Weight	Reps	Weight	Reps	Weight	Reps

TUESDAY

Focus area	Equipment	SET 1		SET 2		SET 3		SET 4	
		Weight	Reps	Weight	Reps	Weight	Reps	Weight	Reps

WEDNESDAY

Focus area	Equipment	SET 1		SET 2		SET 3		SET 4	
		Weight	Reps	Weight	Reps	Weight	Reps	Weight	Reps

THURSDAY

Focus area	Equipment	SET 1		SET 2		SET 3		SET 4	
		Weight	Reps	Weight	Reps	Weight	Reps	Weight	Reps

FRIDAY

Focus area	Equipment	SET 1		SET 2		SET 3		SET 4	
		Weight	Reps	Weight	Reps	Weight	Reps	Weight	Reps

SATURDAY

Focus area	Equipment	SET 1		SET 2		SET 3		SET 4	
		Weight	Reps	Weight	Reps	Weight	Reps	Weight	Reps

SUNDAY

Focus area	Equipment	SET 1		SET 2		SET 3		SET 4	
		Weight	Reps	Weight	Reps	Weight	Reps	Weight	Reps

Cardio Training

MONDAY

Exercise	Time	Distance/ resistance	Intensity	Heart rate	Ease	Cal/kJ expended
						Total:

TUESDAY

Exercise	Time	Distance/ resistance	Intensity	Heart rate	Ease	Cal/kJ expended
						Total:

WEDNESDAY

Exercise	Time	Distance/ resistance	Intensity	Heart rate	Ease	Cal/kJ expended
						Total:

THURSDAY

Exercise	Time	Distance/ resistance	Intensity	Heart rate	Ease	Cal/kJ expended
						Total:

FRIDAY

Exercise	Time	Distance/ resistance	Intensity	Heart rate	Ease	Cal/kJ expended
						Total:

SATURDAY

Exercise	Time	Distance/ resistance	Intensity	Heart rate	Ease	Cal/kJ expended
						Total:

SUNDAY

Exercise	Time	Distance/ resistance	Intensity	Heart rate	Ease	Cal/kJ expended
						Total:
					Weekly Total:	

Food Diary

MONDAY		Cal/kJ	Fat	Protein	Carbs
Breakfast time: am/pm					
Lunch time: am/pm					
Dinner time: am/pm					
Snacks:					
Coffees/teas:	Fluid intake: **Totals:**				

TUESDAY		Cal/kJ	Fat	Protein	Carbs
Breakfast time: am/pm					
Lunch time: am/pm					
Dinner time: am/pm					
Snacks:					
Coffees/teas:	Fluid intake: **Totals:**				

WEDNESDAY		Cal/kJ	Fat	Protein	Carbs
Breakfast time: am/pm					
Lunch time: am/pm					
Dinner time: am/pm					
Snacks:					
Coffees/teas:	Fluid intake: **Totals:**				

THURSDAY		Cal/kJ	Fat	Protein	Carbs
Breakfast time: am/pm					
Lunch time: am/pm					
Dinner time: am/pm					
Snacks:					
Coffees/teas:	Fluid intake: **Totals:**				

FRIDAY		Cal/kJ	Fat	Protein	Carbs
Breakfast time: am/pm					
Lunch time: am/pm					
Dinner time: am/pm					
Snacks:					
Coffees/teas:	Fluid intake: **Totals:**				

SATURDAY		Cal/kJ	Fat	Protein	Carbs
Breakfast time: am/pm					
Lunch time: am/pm					
Dinner time: am/pm					
Snacks:					
Coffees/teas:	Fluid intake: **Totals:**				

SUNDAY		Cal/kJ	Fat	Protein	Carbs
Breakfast time: am/pm					
Lunch time: am/pm					
Dinner time: am/pm					
Snacks:					
Coffees/teas:	Fluid intake: **Totals:**				

Units of alcohol this week: Total alcohol Cal/kJ:

Vitamins and supplements

	Cal/kJ	Fat	Protein	Carbs
Weekly Totals				

Weekly Personal Summary

Energy level (1–5)

Stress level (1–5)

Hours of sleep

Sleep quality (1–5)

Mood (1–5)

Appetite (1–5)

Cal/kJ intake

Planned Cal/kJ	
Actual Cal/kJ	
Difference [+/-]	

Weight at start of week

Weight at end of week

BMI at start of week

BMI at end of week

Injuries or illnesses

Week Beginning

/ /

Planned exercise sessions this week

	Exercise	Completed [Y/N]
Monday		
Tuesday		
Wednesday		
Thursday		
Friday		
Saturday		
Sunday		

Strength Training

MONDAY	ocus area	Equipment	SET 1		SET 2		SET 3		SET 4	
			Weight	Reps	Weight	Reps	Weight	Reps	Weight	Reps

TUESDAY	ocus area	Equipment	SET 1		SET 2		SET 3		SET 4	
			Weight	Reps	Weight	Reps	Weight	Reps	Weight	Reps

WEDNESDAY	ocus area	Equipment	SET 1		SET 2		SET 3		SET 4	
			Weight	Reps	Weight	Reps	Weight	Reps	Weight	Reps

THURSDAY	ocus area	Equipment	SET 1		SET 2		SET 3		SET 4	
			Weight	Reps	Weight	Reps	Weight	Reps	Weight	Reps

FRIDAY	ocus area	Equipment	SET 1		SET 2		SET 3		SET 4	
			Weight	Reps	Weight	Reps	Weight	Reps	Weight	Reps

SATURDAY	ocus area	Equipment	SET 1		SET 2		SET 3		SET 4	
			Weight	Reps	Weight	Reps	Weight	Reps	Weight	Reps

SUNDAY	ocus area	Equipment	SET 1		SET 2		SET 3		SET 4	
			Weight	Reps	Weight	Reps	Weight	Reps	Weight	Reps

Cardio Training

MONDAY

Exercise	Time	Distance/ resistance	Intensity	Heart rate	Ease	Cal/kJ expended
						Total:

TUESDAY

Exercise	Time	Distance/ resistance	Intensity	Heart rate	Ease	Cal/kJ expended
						Total:

WEDNESDAY

Exercise	Time	Distance/ resistance	Intensity	Heart rate	Ease	Cal/kJ expended
						Total:

THURSDAY

Exercise	Time	Distance/ resistance	Intensity	Heart rate	Ease	Cal/kJ expended
						Total:

FRIDAY

Exercise	Time	Distance/ resistance	Intensity	Heart rate	Ease	Cal/kJ expended
						Total:

SATURDAY

Exercise	Time	Distance/ resistance	Intensity	Heart rate	Ease	Cal/kJ expended
						Total:

SUNDAY

Exercise	Time	Distance/ resistance	Intensity	Heart rate	Ease	Cal/kJ expended
						Total:
						Weekly Total:

Food Diary

MONDAY		Cal/kJ	Fat	Protein	Carbs
Breakfast time: am/pm					
Lunch time: am/pm					
Dinner time: am/pm					
Snacks:					
Coffees/teas:	Fluid intake: **Totals:**				

TUESDAY		Cal/kJ	Fat	Protein	Carbs
Breakfast time: am/pm					
Lunch time: am/pm					
Dinner time: am/pm					
Snacks:					
Coffees/teas:	Fluid intake: **Totals:**				

WEDNESDAY		Cal/kJ	Fat	Protein	Carbs
Breakfast time: am/pm					
Lunch time: am/pm					
Dinner time: am/pm					
Snacks:					
Coffees/teas:	Fluid intake: **Totals:**				

THURSDAY		Cal/kJ	Fat	Protein	Carbs
Breakfast time: am/pm					
Lunch time: am/pm					
Dinner time: am/pm					
Snacks:					
Coffees/teas:	Fluid intake: **Totals:**				

FRIDAY			Cal/kJ	Fat	Protein	Carbs
Breakfast time: am/pm						
Lunch time: am/pm						
Dinner time: am/pm						
Snacks:						
Coffees/teas:	Fluid intake:	**Totals:**				

SATURDAY			Cal/kJ	Fat	Protein	Carbs
Breakfast time: am/pm						
Lunch time: am/pm						
Dinner time: am/pm						
Snacks:						
Coffees/teas:	Fluid intake:	**Totals:**				

SUNDAY			Cal/kJ	Fat	Protein	Carbs
Breakfast time: am/pm						
Lunch time: am/pm						
Dinner time: am/pm						
Snacks:						
Coffees/teas:	Fluid intake:	**Totals:**				

Units of alcohol this week: Total alcohol Cal/kJ:

Vitamins and supplements

Weekly Totals	Cal/kJ	Fat	Protein	Carbs

Weekly Personal Summary

Energy level 1–5

Stress level 1–5

Hours of sleep

Sleep quality 1–5

Mood 1–5

Appetite 1–5

Cal/kJ intake

Planned Cal/kJ	
Actual Cal/kJ	
Difference [+/-]	

Weight at start of week

Weight at end of week

BMI at start of week

BMI at end of week

Injuries or illnesses

Week Beginning

/ /

Planned exercise sessions this week

	Exercise	Completed [Y/N]
Monday		
Tuesday		
Wednesday		
Thursday		
Friday		
Saturday		
Sunday		

Strength Training

MONDAY	Focus area	Equipment	SET 1		SET 2		SET 3		SET 4	
			Weight	Reps	Weight	Reps	Weight	Reps	Weight	Reps

TUESDAY	Focus area	Equipment	SET 1		SET 2		SET 3		SET 4	
			Weight	Reps	Weight	Reps	Weight	Reps	Weight	Reps

WEDNESDAY	Focus area	Equipment	SET 1		SET 2		SET 3		SET 4	
			Weight	Reps	Weight	Reps	Weight	Reps	Weight	Reps

THURSDAY	Focus area	Equipment	SET 1		SET 2		SET 3		SET 4	
			Weight	Reps	Weight	Reps	Weight	Reps	Weight	Reps

FRIDAY	Focus area	Equipment	SET 1		SET 2		SET 3		SET 4	
			Weight	Reps	Weight	Reps	Weight	Reps	Weight	Reps

SATURDAY	Focus area	Equipment	SET 1		SET 2		SET 3		SET 4	
			Weight	Reps	Weight	Reps	Weight	Reps	Weight	Reps

SUNDAY	Focus area	Equipment	SET 1		SET 2		SET 3		SET 4	
			Weight	Reps	Weight	Reps	Weight	Reps	Weight	Reps

Cardio Training

MONDAY	Exercise	Time	Distance/ resistance	Intensity	Heart rate	Ease	Cal/kJ expended
							Total:

TUESDAY	Exercise	Time	Distance/ resistance	Intensity	Heart rate	Ease	Cal/kJ expended
							Total:

WEDNESDAY	Exercise	Time	Distance/ resistance	Intensity	Heart rate	Ease	Cal/kJ expended
							Total:

THURSDAY	Exercise	Time	Distance/ resistance	Intensity	Heart rate	Ease	Cal/kJ expended
							Total:

FRIDAY	Exercise	Time	Distance/ resistance	Intensity	Heart rate	Ease	Cal/kJ expended
							Total:

SATURDAY	Exercise	Time	Distance/ resistance	Intensity	Heart rate	Ease	Cal/kJ expended
							Total:

SUNDAY	Exercise	Time	Distance/ resistance	Intensity	Heart rate	Ease	Cal/kJ expended
							Total:
						Weekly Total:	

Food Diary

MONDAY		Cal/kJ	Fat	Protein	Carbs
Breakfast time: am/pm					
Lunch time: am/pm					
Dinner time: am/pm					
Snacks:					
Coffees/teas:	Fluid intake: **Totals:**				

TUESDAY		Cal/kJ	Fat	Protein	Carbs
Breakfast time: am/pm					
Lunch time: am/pm					
Dinner time: am/pm					
Snacks:					
Coffees/teas:	Fluid intake: **Totals:**				

WEDNESDAY		Cal/kJ	Fat	Protein	Carbs
Breakfast time: am/pm					
Lunch time: am/pm					
Dinner time: am/pm					
Snacks:					
Coffees/teas:	Fluid intake: **Totals:**				

THURSDAY		Cal/kJ	Fat	Protein	Carbs
Breakfast time: am/pm					
Lunch time: am/pm					
Dinner time: am/pm					
Snacks:					
Coffees/teas:	Fluid intake: **Totals:**				

FRIDAY			Cal/kJ	Fat	Protein	Carbs
Breakfast time: am/pm						
Lunch time: am/pm						
Dinner time: am/pm						
Snacks:						
Coffees/teas:	Fluid intake:	**Totals:**				

SATURDAY			Cal/kJ	Fat	Protein	Carbs
Breakfast time: am/pm						
Lunch time: am/pm						
Dinner time: am/pm						
Snacks:						
Coffees/teas:	Fluid intake:	**Totals:**				

SUNDAY			Cal/kJ	Fat	Protein	Carbs
Breakfast time: am/pm						
Lunch time: am/pm						
Dinner time: am/pm						
Snacks:						
Coffees/teas:	Fluid intake:	**Totals:**				

Units of alcohol this week: ____ Total alcohol Cal/kJ: ____

Vitamins and supplements

Weekly Totals	Cal/kJ	Fat	Protein	Carbs

Weekly Personal Summary

Energy level (1–5) ____ Stress level (1–5) ____

Hours of sleep ____ Sleep quality (1–5) ____

Mood (1–5) ____ Appetite (1–5) ____

Cal/kJ intake

Planned Cal/kJ	
Actual Cal/kJ	

Difference [+/-] ____

Weight at start of week ____

Weight at end of week ____

BMI at start of week ____

BMI at end of week ____

Injuries or illnesses ____

Week Beginning

/ /

Planned exercise sessions this week

	Exercise	Completed [Y/N]
Monday		
Tuesday		
Wednesday		
Thursday		
Friday		
Saturday		
Sunday		

Strength Training

MONDAY	Focus area	Equipment	SET 1		SET 2		SET 3		SET 4	
			Weight	Reps	Weight	Reps	Weight	Reps	Weight	Reps

TUESDAY	Focus area	Equipment	SET 1		SET 2		SET 3		SET 4	
			Weight	Reps	Weight	Reps	Weight	Reps	Weight	Reps

WEDNESDAY	Focus area	Equipment	SET 1		SET 2		SET 3		SET 4	
			Weight	Reps	Weight	Reps	Weight	Reps	Weight	Reps

THURSDAY	Focus area	Equipment	SET 1		SET 2		SET 3		SET 4	
			Weight	Reps	Weight	Reps	Weight	Reps	Weight	Reps

FRIDAY	Focus area	Equipment	SET 1		SET 2		SET 3		SET 4	
			Weight	Reps	Weight	Reps	Weight	Reps	Weight	Reps

SATURDAY	Focus area	Equipment	SET 1		SET 2		SET 3		SET 4	
			Weight	Reps	Weight	Reps	Weight	Reps	Weight	Reps

SUNDAY	Focus area	Equipment	SET 1		SET 2		SET 3		SET 4	
			Weight	Reps	Weight	Reps	Weight	Reps	Weight	Reps

Cardio Training

MONDAY

Exercise	Time	Distance/ resistance	Intensity	Heart rate	Ease	Cal/kJ expended
						Total:

TUESDAY

Exercise	Time	Distance/ resistance	Intensity	Heart rate	Ease	Cal/kJ expended
						Total:

WEDNESDAY

Exercise	Time	Distance/ resistance	Intensity	Heart rate	Ease	Cal/kJ expended
						Total:

THURSDAY

Exercise	Time	Distance/ resistance	Intensity	Heart rate	Ease	Cal/kJ expended
						Total:

FRIDAY

Exercise	Time	Distance/ resistance	Intensity	Heart rate	Ease	Cal/kJ expended
						Total:

SATURDAY

Exercise	Time	Distance/ resistance	Intensity	Heart rate	Ease	Cal/kJ expended
						Total:

SUNDAY

Exercise	Time	Distance/ resistance	Intensity	Heart rate	Ease	Cal/kJ expended
						Total:

Weekly Total:

Food Diary

MONDAY		Cal/kJ	Fat	Protein	Carbs
Breakfast time: am/pm					
Lunch time: am/pm					
Dinner time: am/pm					
Snacks:					
Coffees/teas:	Fluid intake: **Totals:**				

TUESDAY		Cal/kJ	Fat	Protein	Carbs
Breakfast time: am/pm					
Lunch time: am/pm					
Dinner time: am/pm					
Snacks:					
Coffees/teas:	Fluid intake: **Totals:**				

WEDNESDAY		Cal/kJ	Fat	Protein	Carbs
Breakfast time: am/pm					
Lunch time: am/pm					
Dinner time: am/pm					
Snacks:					
Coffees/teas:	Fluid intake: **Totals:**				

THURSDAY		Cal/kJ	Fat	Protein	Carbs
Breakfast time: am/pm					
Lunch time: am/pm					
Dinner time: am/pm					
Snacks:					
Coffees/teas:	Fluid intake: **Totals:**				

FRIDAY		Cal/kJ	Fat	Protein	Carbs
Breakfast time: am/pm					
Lunch time: am/pm					
Dinner time: am/pm					
Snacks:					
Coffees/teas:	Fluid intake: **Totals:**				

SATURDAY		Cal/kJ	Fat	Protein	Carbs
Breakfast time: am/pm					
Lunch time: am/pm					
Dinner time: am/pm					
Snacks:					
Coffees/teas:	Fluid intake: **Totals:**				

SUNDAY		Cal/kJ	Fat	Protein	Carbs
Breakfast time: am/pm					
Lunch time: am/pm					
Dinner time: am/pm					
Snacks:					
Coffees/teas:	Fluid intake: **Totals:**				

Units of alcohol this week: Total alcohol Cal/kJ:

Vitamins and supplements

Weekly Totals	Cal/kJ	Fat	Protein	Carbs

Weekly Personal Summary

Energy level 1–5

Stress level 1–5

Hours of sleep

Sleep quality 1–5

Mood 1–5

Appetite 1–5

Cal/kJ intake

Planned Cal/kJ	
Actual Cal/kJ	

Difference [+/-]

Weight at start of week

Weight at end of week

BMI at start of week

BMI at end of week

Injuries or illnesses

Week Beginning

/ /

Strength Training

Planned exercise sessions this week

	Exercise	Completed [Y/N]
Monday		
Tuesday		
Wednesday		
Thursday		
Friday		
Saturday		
Sunday		

MONDAY

Focus area	Equipment	SET 1		SET 2		SET 3		SET 4	
		Weight	Reps	Weight	Reps	Weight	Reps	Weight	Reps

TUESDAY

Focus area	Equipment	SET 1		SET 2		SET 3		SET 4	
		Weight	Reps	Weight	Reps	Weight	Reps	Weight	Reps

WEDNESDAY

Focus area	Equipment	SET 1		SET 2		SET 3		SET 4	
		Weight	Reps	Weight	Reps	Weight	Reps	Weight	Reps

THURSDAY

Focus area	Equipment	SET 1		SET 2		SET 3		SET 4	
		Weight	Reps	Weight	Reps	Weight	Reps	Weight	Reps

FRIDAY

Focus area	Equipment	SET 1		SET 2		SET 3		SET 4	
		Weight	Reps	Weight	Reps	Weight	Reps	Weight	Reps

SATURDAY

Focus area	Equipment	SET 1		SET 2		SET 3		SET 4	
		Weight	Reps	Weight	Reps	Weight	Reps	Weight	Reps

SUNDAY

Focus area	Equipment	SET 1		SET 2		SET 3		SET 4	
		Weight	Reps	Weight	Reps	Weight	Reps	Weight	Reps

Cardio Training

MONDAY

Exercise	Time	Distance/ resistance	Intensity	Heart rate	Ease	Cal/kJ expended
						Total:

TUESDAY

Exercise	Time	Distance/ resistance	Intensity	Heart rate	Ease	Cal/kJ expended
						Total:

WEDNESDAY

Exercise	Time	Distance/ resistance	Intensity	Heart rate	Ease	Cal/kJ expended
						Total:

THURSDAY

Exercise	Time	Distance/ resistance	Intensity	Heart rate	Ease	Cal/kJ expended
						Total:

FRIDAY

Exercise	Time	Distance/ resistance	Intensity	Heart rate	Ease	Cal/kJ expended
						Total:

SATURDAY

Exercise	Time	Distance/ resistance	Intensity	Heart rate	Ease	Cal/kJ expended
						Total:

SUNDAY

Exercise	Time	Distance/ resistance	Intensity	Heart rate	Ease	Cal/kJ expended
						Total:
						Weekly Total:

Food Diary

MONDAY			Cal/kJ	Fat	Protein	Carbs
Breakfast time: am/pm						
Lunch time: am/pm						
Dinner time: am/pm						
Snacks:						
Coffees/teas:	Fluid intake:	**Totals:**				

TUESDAY			Cal/kJ	Fat	Protein	Carbs
Breakfast time: am/pm						
Lunch time: am/pm						
Dinner time: am/pm						
Snacks:						
Coffees/teas:	Fluid intake:	**Totals:**				

WEDNESDAY			Cal/kJ	Fat	Protein	Carbs
Breakfast time: am/pm						
Lunch time: am/pm						
Dinner time: am/pm						
Snacks:						
Coffees/teas:	Fluid intake:	**Totals:**				

THURSDAY			Cal/kJ	Fat	Protein	Carbs
Breakfast time: am/pm						
Lunch time: am/pm						
Dinner time: am/pm						
Snacks:						
Coffees/teas:	Fluid intake:	**Totals:**				

FRIDAY		Cal/kJ	Fat	Protein	Carbs
Breakfast time: am/pm					
Lunch time: am/pm					
Dinner time: am/pm					
Snacks:					
Coffees/teas:	Fluid intake: **Totals:**				

SATURDAY		Cal/kJ	Fat	Protein	Carbs
Breakfast time: am/pm					
Lunch time: am/pm					
Dinner time: am/pm					
Snacks:					
Coffees/teas:	Fluid intake: **Totals:**				

SUNDAY		Cal/kJ	Fat	Protein	Carbs
Breakfast time: am/pm					
Lunch time: am/pm					
Dinner time: am/pm					
Snacks:					
Coffees/teas:	Fluid intake: **Totals:**				

Units of alcohol this week: Total alcohol Cal/kJ:

Vitamins and supplements

Weekly Totals	Cal/kJ	Fat	Protein	Carbs

Weekly Personal Summary

Energy level 1–5

Stress level 1–5

Hours of sleep

Sleep quality 1–5

Mood 1–5

Appetite 1–5

Cal/kJ intake

Planned Cal/kJ	
Actual Cal/kJ	

Difference [+/-]

Weight at start of week

Weight at end of week

BMI at start of week

BMI at end of week

Injuries or illnesses

Week Beginning

/ /

Planned exercise sessions this week

	Exercise	Completed [Y/N]
Monday		
Tuesday		
Wednesday		
Thursday		
Friday		
Saturday		
Sunday		

Strength Training

MONDAY	Focus area	Equipment	SET 1		SET 2		SET 3		SET 4	
			Weight	Reps	Weight	Reps	Weight	Reps	Weight	Reps

TUESDAY	Focus area	Equipment	SET 1		SET 2		SET 3		SET 4	
			Weight	Reps	Weight	Reps	Weight	Reps	Weight	Reps

WEDNESDAY	Focus area	Equipment	SET 1		SET 2		SET 3		SET 4	
			Weight	Reps	Weight	Reps	Weight	Reps	Weight	Reps

THURSDAY	Focus area	Equipment	SET 1		SET 2		SET 3		SET 4	
			Weight	Reps	Weight	Reps	Weight	Reps	Weight	Reps

FRIDAY	Focus area	Equipment	SET 1		SET 2		SET 3		SET 4	
			Weight	Reps	Weight	Reps	Weight	Reps	Weight	Reps

SATURDAY	Focus area	Equipment	SET 1		SET 2		SET 3		SET 4	
			Weight	Reps	Weight	Reps	Weight	Reps	Weight	Reps

SUNDAY	Focus area	Equipment	SET 1		SET 2		SET 3		SET 4	
			Weight	Reps	Weight	Reps	Weight	Reps	Weight	Reps

Cardio Training

MONDAY

Exercise	Time	Distance/ resistance	Intensity	Heart rate	Ease	Cal/kJ expended
						Total:

TUESDAY

Exercise	Time	Distance/ resistance	Intensity	Heart rate	Ease	Cal/kJ expended
						Total:

WEDNESDAY

Exercise	Time	Distance/ resistance	Intensity	Heart rate	Ease	Cal/kJ expended
						Total:

THURSDAY

Exercise	Time	Distance/ resistance	Intensity	Heart rate	Ease	Cal/kJ expended
						Total:

FRIDAY

Exercise	Time	Distance/ resistance	Intensity	Heart rate	Ease	Cal/kJ expended
						Total:

SATURDAY

Exercise	Time	Distance/ resistance	Intensity	Heart rate	Ease	Cal/kJ expended
						Total:

SUNDAY

Exercise	Time	Distance/ resistance	Intensity	Heart rate	Ease	Cal/kJ expended
						Total:
						Weekly Total:

Food Diary

MONDAY			Cal/kJ	Fat	Protein	Carbs
Breakfast time: am/pm						
Lunch time: am/pm						
Dinner time: am/pm						
Snacks:						
Coffees/teas:	Fluid intake:	**Totals:**				

TUESDAY			Cal/kJ	Fat	Protein	Carbs
Breakfast time: am/pm						
Lunch time: am/pm						
Dinner time: am/pm						
Snacks:						
Coffees/teas:	Fluid intake:	**Totals:**				

WEDNESDAY			Cal/kJ	Fat	Protein	Carbs
Breakfast time: am/pm						
Lunch time: am/pm						
Dinner time: am/pm						
Snacks:						
Coffees/teas:	Fluid intake:	**Totals:**				

THURSDAY			Cal/kJ	Fat	Protein	Carbs
Breakfast time: am/pm						
Lunch time: am/pm						
Dinner time: am/pm						
Snacks:						
Coffees/teas:	Fluid intake:	**Totals:**				

FRIDAY			Cal/kJ	Fat	Protein	Carbs
Breakfast time: am/pm						
Lunch time: am/pm						
Dinner time: am/pm						
Snacks:						
Coffees/teas:	Fluid intake:	**Totals:**				

SATURDAY			Cal/kJ	Fat	Protein	Carbs
Breakfast time: am/pm						
Lunch time: am/pm						
Dinner time: am/pm						
Snacks:						
Coffees/teas:	Fluid intake:	**Totals:**				

SUNDAY			Cal/kJ	Fat	Protein	Carbs
Breakfast time: am/pm						
Lunch time: am/pm						
Dinner time: am/pm						
Snacks:						
Coffees/teas:	Fluid intake:	**Totals:**				

Units of alcohol this week: Total alcohol Cal/kJ:

Vitamins and supplements

	Cal/kJ	Fat	Protein	Carbs
Weekly Totals				

Weekly Personal Summary

Energy level (1–5) Stress level (1–5)

Hours of sleep Sleep quality (1–5)

Mood (1–5) Appetite (1–5)

Cal/kJ intake

Planned Cal/kJ	
Actual Cal/kJ	
Difference [+/-]	

Weight at start of week

Weight at end of week

BMI at start of week

BMI at end of week

Injuries or illnesses

Week Beginning

/ /

Strength Training

Planned exercise sessions this week

	Exercise	Completed [Y/N]
Monday		
Tuesday		
Wednesday		
Thursday		
Friday		
Saturday		
Sunday		

	Focus area	Equipment	SET 1		SET 2		SET 3		SET 4	
			Weight	Reps	Weight	Reps	Weight	Reps	Weight	Reps
MONDAY										

	Focus area	Equipment	SET 1		SET 2		SET 3		SET 4	
			Weight	Reps	Weight	Reps	Weight	Reps	Weight	Reps
TUESDAY										

	Focus area	Equipment	SET 1		SET 2		SET 3		SET 4	
			Weight	Reps	Weight	Reps	Weight	Reps	Weight	Reps
WEDNESDAY										

	Focus area	Equipment	SET 1		SET 2		SET 3		SET 4	
			Weight	Reps	Weight	Reps	Weight	Reps	Weight	Reps
THURSDAY										

	Focus area	Equipment	SET 1		SET 2		SET 3		SET 4	
			Weight	Reps	Weight	Reps	Weight	Reps	Weight	Reps
FRIDAY										

	Focus area	Equipment	SET 1		SET 2		SET 3		SET 4	
			Weight	Reps	Weight	Reps	Weight	Reps	Weight	Reps
SATURDAY										

	Focus area	Equipment	SET 1		SET 2		SET 3		SET 4	
			Weight	Reps	Weight	Reps	Weight	Reps	Weight	Reps
SUNDAY										

Cardio Training

MONDAY	Exercise	Time	Distance/ resistance	Intensity	Heart rate	Ease	Cal/kJ expended
							Total:

TUESDAY	Exercise	Time	Distance/ resistance	Intensity	Heart rate	Ease	Cal/kJ expended
							Total:

WEDNESDAY	Exercise	Time	Distance/ resistance	Intensity	Heart rate	Ease	Cal/kJ expended
							Total:

THURSDAY	Exercise	Time	Distance/ resistance	Intensity	Heart rate	Ease	Cal/kJ expended
							Total:

FRIDAY	Exercise	Time	Distance/ resistance	Intensity	Heart rate	Ease	Cal/kJ expended
							Total:

SATURDAY	Exercise	Time	Distance/ resistance	Intensity	Heart rate	Ease	Cal/kJ expended
							Total:

SUNDAY	Exercise	Time	Distance/ resistance	Intensity	Heart rate	Ease	Cal/kJ expended
							Total:
							Weekly Total:

Food Diary

MONDAY		Cal/kJ	Fat	Protein	Carbs
Breakfast time: am/pm					
Lunch time: am/pm					
Dinner time: am/pm					
Snacks:					
Coffees/teas:	Fluid intake: **Totals:**				

TUESDAY		Cal/kJ	Fat	Protein	Carbs
Breakfast time: am/pm					
Lunch time: am/pm					
Dinner time: am/pm					
Snacks:					
Coffees/teas:	Fluid intake: **Totals:**				

WEDNESDAY		Cal/kJ	Fat	Protein	Carbs
Breakfast time: am/pm					
Lunch time: am/pm					
Dinner time: am/pm					
Snacks:					
Coffees/teas:	Fluid intake: **Totals:**				

THURSDAY		Cal/kJ	Fat	Protein	Carbs
Breakfast time: am/pm					
Lunch time: am/pm					
Dinner time: am/pm					
Snacks:					
Coffees/teas:	Fluid intake: **Totals:**				

FRIDAY			Cal/kJ	Fat	Protein	Carbs
Breakfast time: am/pm						
Lunch time: am/pm						
Dinner time: am/pm						
Snacks:						
Coffees/teas:	Fluid intake:	**Totals:**				

SATURDAY			Cal/kJ	Fat	Protein	Carbs
Breakfast time: am/pm						
Lunch time: am/pm						
Dinner time: am/pm						
Snacks:						
Coffees/teas:	Fluid intake:	**Totals:**				

SUNDAY			Cal/kJ	Fat	Protein	Carbs
Breakfast time: am/pm						
Lunch time: am/pm						
Dinner time: am/pm						
Snacks:						
Coffees/teas:	Fluid intake:	**Totals:**				

Units of alcohol this week: Total alcohol Cal/kJ:

Vitamins and supplements

	Cal/kJ	Fat	Protein	Carbs
Weekly Totals				

Weekly Personal Summary

Energy level (1–5)

Stress level (1–5)

Hours of sleep

Sleep quality (1–5)

Mood (1–5)

Appetite (1–5)

Cal/kJ intake

Planned Cal/kJ	
Actual Cal/kJ	

Difference [+/-]

Weight at start of week

Weight at end of week

BMI at start of week

BMI at end of week

Injuries or illnesses

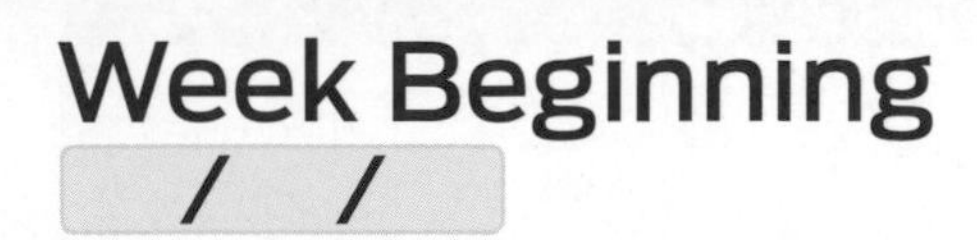

Strength Training

Planned exercise sessions this week

	Exercise	Completed [Y/N]
Monday		
Tuesday		
Wednesday		
Thursday		
Friday		
Saturday		
Sunday		

MONDAY	ocus area	Equipment	SET 1		SET 2		SET 3		SET 4	
			Weight	Reps	Weight	Reps	Weight	Reps	Weight	Reps

TUESDAY	ocus area	Equipment	SET 1		SET 2		SET 3		SET 4	
			Weight	Reps	Weight	Reps	Weight	Reps	Weight	Reps

WEDNESDAY	ocus area	Equipment	SET 1		SET 2		SET 3		SET 4	
			Weight	Reps	Weight	Reps	Weight	Reps	Weight	Reps

THURSDAY	ocus area	Equipment	SET 1		SET 2		SET 3		SET 4	
			Weight	Reps	Weight	Reps	Weight	Reps	Weight	Reps

FRIDAY	ocus area	Equipment	SET 1		SET 2		SET 3		SET 4	
			Weight	Reps	Weight	Reps	Weight	Reps	Weight	Reps

SATURDAY	ocus area	Equipment	SET 1		SET 2		SET 3		SET 4	
			Weight	Reps	Weight	Reps	Weight	Reps	Weight	Reps

SUNDAY	ocus area	Equipment	SET 1		SET 2		SET 3		SET 4	
			Weight	Reps	Weight	Reps	Weight	Reps	Weight	Reps

Cardio Training

MONDAY	Exercise	Time	Distance/ resistance	Intensity	Heart rate	Ease	Cal/kJ expended
							Total:

TUESDAY	Exercise	Time	Distance/ resistance	Intensity	Heart rate	Ease	Cal/kJ expended
							Total:

WEDNESDAY	Exercise	Time	Distance/ resistance	Intensity	Heart rate	Ease	Cal/kJ expended
							Total:

THURSDAY	Exercise	Time	Distance/ resistance	Intensity	Heart rate	Ease	Cal/kJ expended
							Total:

FRIDAY	Exercise	Time	Distance/ resistance	Intensity	Heart rate	Ease	Cal/kJ expended
							Total:

SATURDAY	Exercise	Time	Distance/ resistance	Intensity	Heart rate	Ease	Cal/kJ expended
							Total:

SUNDAY	Exercise	Time	Distance/ resistance	Intensity	Heart rate	Ease	Cal/kJ expended
							Total:
							Weekly Total:

Food Diary

MONDAY		Cal/kJ	Fat	Protein	Carbs
Breakfast time: am/pm					
Lunch time: am/pm					
Dinner time: am/pm					
Snacks:					
Coffees/teas:	Fluid intake: **Totals:**				

TUESDAY		Cal/kJ	Fat	Protein	Carbs
Breakfast time: am/pm					
Lunch time: am/pm					
Dinner time: am/pm					
Snacks:					
Coffees/teas:	Fluid intake: **Totals:**				

WEDNESDAY		Cal/kJ	Fat	Protein	Carbs
Breakfast time: am/pm					
Lunch time: am/pm					
Dinner time: am/pm					
Snacks:					
Coffees/teas:	Fluid intake: **Totals:**				

THURSDAY		Cal/kJ	Fat	Protein	Carbs
Breakfast time: am/pm					
Lunch time: am/pm					
Dinner time: am/pm					
Snacks:					
Coffees/teas:	Fluid intake: **Totals:**				

FRIDAY			Cal/kJ	Fat	Protein	Carbs
Breakfast time: am/pm						
Lunch time: am/pm						
Dinner time: am/pm						
Snacks:						
Coffees/teas:	Fluid intake:	**Totals:**				

SATURDAY			Cal/kJ	Fat	Protein	Carbs
Breakfast time: am/pm						
Lunch time: am/pm						
Dinner time: am/pm						
Snacks:						
Coffees/teas:	Fluid intake:	**Totals:**				

SUNDAY			Cal/kJ	Fat	Protein	Carbs
Breakfast time: am/pm						
Lunch time: am/pm						
Dinner time: am/pm						
Snacks:						
Coffees/teas:	Fluid intake:	**Totals:**				

Units of alcohol this week: Total alcohol Cal/kJ:

Vitamins and supplements

Weekly Totals	Cal/kJ	Fat	Protein	Carbs

Weekly Personal Summary

Energy level (1–5)

Stress level (1–5)

Hours of sleep

Sleep quality (1–5)

Mood (1–5)

Appetite (1–5)

Cal/kJ intake

Planned Cal/kJ	
Actual Cal/kJ	
Difference [+/-]	

Weight at start of week

Weight at end of week

BMI at start of week

BMI at end of week

Injuries or illnesses

Week Beginning

/ /

Planned exercise sessions this week

	Exercise	Completed [Y/N]
Monday		
Tuesday		
Wednesday		
Thursday		
Friday		
Saturday		
Sunday		

Strength Training

MONDAY

ocus area	Equipment	SET 1		SET 2		SET 3		SET 4	
		Weight	Reps	Weight	Reps	Weight	Reps	Weight	Reps

TUESDAY

ocus area	Equipment	SET 1		SET 2		SET 3		SET 4	
		Weight	Reps	Weight	Reps	Weight	Reps	Weight	Reps

WEDNESDAY

ocus area	Equipment	SET 1		SET 2		SET 3		SET 4	
		Weight	Reps	Weight	Reps	Weight	Reps	Weight	Reps

THURSDAY

ocus area	Equipment	SET 1		SET 2		SET 3		SET 4	
		Weight	Reps	Weight	Reps	Weight	Reps	Weight	Reps

FRIDAY

ocus area	Equipment	SET 1		SET 2		SET 3		SET 4	
		Weight	Reps	Weight	Reps	Weight	Reps	Weight	Reps

SATURDAY

ocus area	Equipment	SET 1		SET 2		SET 3		SET 4	
		Weight	Reps	Weight	Reps	Weight	Reps	Weight	Reps

SUNDAY

Focus area	Equipment	SET 1		SET 2		SET 3		SET 4	
		Weight	Reps	Weight	Reps	Weight	Reps	Weight	Reps

Cardio Training

MONDAY

Exercise	Time	Distance/ resistance	Intensity	Heart rate	Ease	Cal/kJ expended
						Total:

TUESDAY

Exercise	Time	Distance/ resistance	Intensity	Heart rate	Ease	Cal/kJ expended
						Total:

WEDNESDAY

Exercise	Time	Distance/ resistance	Intensity	Heart rate	Ease	Cal/kJ expended
						Total:

THURSDAY

Exercise	Time	Distance/ resistance	Intensity	Heart rate	Ease	Cal/kJ expended
						Total:

FRIDAY

Exercise	Time	Distance/ resistance	Intensity	Heart rate	Ease	Cal/kJ expended
						Total:

SATURDAY

Exercise	Time	Distance/ resistance	Intensity	Heart rate	Ease	Cal/kJ expended
						Total:

SUNDAY

Exercise	Time	Distance/ resistance	Intensity	Heart rate	Ease	Cal/kJ expended
						Total:
						Weekly Total:

Food Diary

MONDAY		Cal/kJ	Fat	Protein	Carbs
Breakfast time: am/pm					
Lunch time: am/pm					
Dinner time: am/pm					
Snacks:					
Coffees/teas:	Fluid intake: **Totals:**				

TUESDAY		Cal/kJ	Fat	Protein	Carbs
Breakfast time: am/pm					
Lunch time: am/pm					
Dinner time: am/pm					
Snacks:					
Coffees/teas:	Fluid intake: **Totals:**				

WEDNESDAY		Cal/kJ	Fat	Protein	Carbs
Breakfast time: am/pm					
Lunch time: am/pm					
Dinner time: am/pm					
Snacks:					
Coffees/teas:	Fluid intake: **Totals:**				

THURSDAY		Cal/kJ	Fat	Protein	Carbs
Breakfast time: am/pm					
Lunch time: am/pm					
Dinner time: am/pm					
Snacks:					
Coffees/teas:	Fluid intake: **Totals:**				

FRIDAY		Cal/kJ	Fat	Protein	Carbs
Breakfast time: am/pm					
Lunch time: am/pm					
Dinner time: am/pm					
Snacks:					
Coffees/teas:	Fluid intake: **Totals:**				

SATURDAY		Cal/kJ	Fat	Protein	Carbs
Breakfast time: am/pm					
Lunch time: am/pm					
Dinner time: am/pm					
Snacks:					
Coffees/teas:	Fluid intake: **Totals:**				

SUNDAY		Cal/kJ	Fat	Protein	Carbs
Breakfast time: am/pm					
Lunch time: am/pm					
Dinner time: am/pm					
Snacks:					
Coffees/teas:	Fluid intake: **Totals:**				

Units of alcohol this week: Total alcohol Cal/kJ:

Vitamins and supplements

Weekly Totals	Cal/kJ	Fat	Protein	Carbs

Weekly Personal Summary

Energy level 1–5 Stress level 1–5

Hours of sleep Sleep quality 1–5

Mood 1–5 Appetite 1–5

Cal/kJ intake

Planned Cal/kJ

Actual Cal/kJ

Difference [+/-]

Weight at start of week

Weight at end of week

BMI at start of week

BMI at end of week

Injuries or illnesses

Week Beginning

/ /

Planned exercise sessions this week

	Exercise	Completed [Y/N]
Monday		
Tuesday		
Wednesday		
Thursday		
Friday		
Saturday		
Sunday		

Strength Training

MONDAY

Focus area	Equipment	SET 1		SET 2		SET 3		SET 4	
		Weight	Reps	Weight	Reps	Weight	Reps	Weight	Reps

TUESDAY

Focus area	Equipment	SET 1		SET 2		SET 3		SET 4	
		Weight	Reps	Weight	Reps	Weight	Reps	Weight	Reps

WEDNESDAY

Focus area	Equipment	SET 1		SET 2		SET 3		SET 4	
		Weight	Reps	Weight	Reps	Weight	Reps	Weight	Reps

THURSDAY

Focus area	Equipment	SET 1		SET 2		SET 3		SET 4	
		Weight	Reps	Weight	Reps	Weight	Reps	Weight	Reps

FRIDAY

Focus area	Equipment	SET 1		SET 2		SET 3		SET 4	
		Weight	Reps	Weight	Reps	Weight	Reps	Weight	Reps

SATURDAY

Focus area	Equipment	SET 1		SET 2		SET 3		SET 4	
		Weight	Reps	Weight	Reps	Weight	Reps	Weight	Reps

SUNDAY

Focus area	Equipment	SET 1		SET 2		SET 3		SET 4	
		Weight	Reps	Weight	Reps	Weight	Reps	Weight	Reps

Cardio Training

MONDAY

Exercise	Time	Distance/ resistance	Intensity	Heart rate	Ease	Cal/kJ expended
						Total:

TUESDAY

Exercise	Time	Distance/ resistance	Intensity	Heart rate	Ease	Cal/kJ expended
						Total:

WEDNESDAY

Exercise	Time	Distance/ resistance	Intensity	Heart rate	Ease	Cal/kJ expended
						Total:

THURSDAY

Exercise	Time	Distance/ resistance	Intensity	Heart rate	Ease	Cal/kJ expended
						Total:

FRIDAY

Exercise	Time	Distance/ resistance	Intensity	Heart rate	Ease	Cal/kJ expended
						Total:

SATURDAY

Exercise	Time	Distance/ resistance	Intensity	Heart rate	Ease	Cal/kJ expended
						Total:

SUNDAY

Exercise	Time	Distance/ resistance	Intensity	Heart rate	Ease	Cal/kJ expended
						Total:

Weekly Total:

Food Diary

MONDAY		Cal/kJ	Fat	Protein	Carbs
Breakfast time: am/pm					
Lunch time: am/pm					
Dinner time: am/pm					
Snacks:					
Coffees/teas:	Fluid intake: **Totals:**				

TUESDAY		Cal/kJ	Fat	Protein	Carbs
Breakfast time: am/pm					
Lunch time: am/pm					
Dinner time: am/pm					
Snacks:					
Coffees/teas:	Fluid intake: **Totals:**				

WEDNESDAY		Cal/kJ	Fat	Protein	Carbs
Breakfast time: am/pm					
Lunch time: am/pm					
Dinner time: am/pm					
Snacks:					
Coffees/teas:	Fluid intake: **Totals:**				

THURSDAY		Cal/kJ	Fat	Protein	Carbs
Breakfast time: am/pm					
Lunch time: am/pm					
Dinner time: am/pm					
Snacks:					
Coffees/teas:	Fluid intake: **Totals:**				

FRIDAY		Cal/kJ	Fat	Protein	Carbs
Breakfast time: am/pm					
Lunch time: am/pm					
Dinner time: am/pm					
Snacks:					
Coffees/teas:	Fluid intake: **Totals:**				

SATURDAY		Cal/kJ	Fat	Protein	Carbs
Breakfast time: am/pm					
Lunch time: am/pm					
Dinner time: am/pm					
Snacks:					
Coffees/teas:	Fluid intake: **Totals:**				

SUNDAY		Cal/kJ	Fat	Protein	Carbs
Breakfast time: am/pm					
Lunch time: am/pm					
Dinner time: am/pm					
Snacks:					
Coffees/teas:	Fluid intake: **Totals:**				

Units of alcohol this week: Total alcohol Cal/kJ:

Vitamins and supplements

Weekly Totals	Cal/kJ	Fat	Protein	Carbs

Weekly Personal Summary

Energy level (1–5)

Stress level (1–5)

Hours of sleep

Sleep quality (1–5)

Mood (1–5)

Appetite (1–5)

Cal/kJ intake

Planned Cal/kJ

Actual Cal/kJ

Difference [+/-]

Weight at start of week

Weight at end of week

BMI at start of week

BMI at end of week

Injuries or illnesses

Week Beginning

/ /

Strength Training

Planned exercise sessions this week

	Exercise	Completed [Y/N]
Monday		
Tuesday		
Wednesday		
Thursday		
Friday		
Saturday		
Sunday		

MONDAY	Focus area	Equipment	SET 1		SET 2		SET 3		SET 4	
			Weight	Reps	Weight	Reps	Weight	Reps	Weight	Reps

TUESDAY	Focus area	Equipment	SET 1		SET 2		SET 3		SET 4	
			Weight	Reps	Weight	Reps	Weight	Reps	Weight	Reps

WEDNESDAY	ocus area	Equipment	SET 1		SET 2		SET 3		SET 4	
			Weight	Reps	Weight	Reps	Weight	Reps	Weight	Reps

THURSDAY	ocus area	Equipment	SET 1		SET 2		SET 3		SET 4	
			Weight	Reps	Weight	Reps	Weight	Reps	Weight	Reps

FRIDAY	Focus area	Equipment	SET 1		SET 2		SET 3		SET 4	
			Weight	Reps	Weight	Reps	Weight	Reps	Weight	Reps

SATURDAY	ocus area	Equipment	SET 1		SET 2		SET 3		SET 4	
			Weight	Reps	Weight	Reps	Weight	Reps	Weight	Reps

SUNDAY	ocus area	Equipment	SET 1		SET 2		SET 3		SET 4	
			Weight	Reps	Weight	Reps	Weight	Reps	Weight	Reps

Cardio Training

MONDAY

Exercise	Time	Distance/ resistance	Intensity	Heart rate	Ease	Cal/kJ expended
						Total:

TUESDAY

Exercise	Time	Distance/ resistance	Intensity	Heart rate	Ease	Cal/kJ expended
						Total:

WEDNESDAY

Exercise	Time	Distance/ resistance	Intensity	Heart rate	Ease	Cal/kJ expended
						Total:

THURSDAY

Exercise	Time	Distance/ resistance	Intensity	Heart rate	Ease	Cal/kJ expended
						Total:

FRIDAY

Exercise	Time	Distance/ resistance	Intensity	Heart rate	Ease	Cal/kJ expended
						Total:

SATURDAY

Exercise	Time	Distance/ resistance	Intensity	Heart rate	Ease	Cal/kJ expended
						Total:

SUNDAY

Exercise	Time	Distance/ resistance	Intensity	Heart rate	Ease	Cal/kJ expended
						Total:
					Weekly Total:	

Food Diary

MONDAY		Cal/kJ	Fat	Protein	Carbs
Breakfast time: am/pm					
Lunch time: am/pm					
Dinner time: am/pm					
Snacks:					
Coffees/teas:	Fluid intake: **Totals:**				

TUESDAY		Cal/kJ	Fat	Protein	Carbs
Breakfast time: am/pm					
Lunch time: am/pm					
Dinner time: am/pm					
Snacks:					
Coffees/teas:	Fluid intake: **Totals:**				

WEDNESDAY		Cal/kJ	Fat	Protein	Carbs
Breakfast time: am/pm					
Lunch time: am/pm					
Dinner time: am/pm					
Snacks:					
Coffees/teas:	Fluid intake: **Totals:**				

THURSDAY		Cal/kJ	Fat	Protein	Carbs
Breakfast time: am/pm					
Lunch time: am/pm					
Dinner time: am/pm					
Snacks:					
Coffees/teas:	Fluid intake: **Totals:**				

FRIDAY		Cal/kJ	Fat	Protein	Carbs
Breakfast time: am/pm					
Lunch time: am/pm					
Dinner time: am/pm					
Snacks:					
Coffees/teas:	Fluid intake: **Totals:**				

SATURDAY		Cal/kJ	Fat	Protein	Carbs
Breakfast time: am/pm					
Lunch time: am/pm					
Dinner time: am/pm					
Snacks:					
Coffees/teas:	Fluid intake: **Totals:**				

SUNDAY		Cal/kJ	Fat	Protein	Carbs
Breakfast time: am/pm					
Lunch time: am/pm					
Dinner time: am/pm					
Snacks:					
Coffees/teas:	Fluid intake: **Totals:**				

Units of alcohol this week: ____ Total alcohol Cal/kJ: ____

Vitamins and supplements

Weekly Totals	Cal/kJ	Fat	Protein	Carbs

Weekly Personal Summary

Energy level (1–5) ____ Stress level (1–5) ____

Hours of sleep ____ Sleep quality (1–5) ____

Mood (1–5) ____ Appetite (1–5) ____

Cal/kJ intake

Planned Cal/kJ	
Actual Cal/kJ	

Difference [+/-] ____

Weight at start of week ____

Weight at end of week ____

BMI at start of week ____

BMI at end of week ____

Injuries or illnesses ____

Week Beginning

/ /

Planned exercise sessions this week

	Exercise	Completed [Y/N]
Monday		
Tuesday		
Wednesday		
Thursday		
Friday		
Saturday		
Sunday		

Strength Training

MONDAY	Focus area	Equipment	SET 1		SET 2		SET 3		SET 4	
			Weight	Reps	Weight	Reps	Weight	Reps	Weight	Reps

TUESDAY	Focus area	Equipment	SET 1		SET 2		SET 3		SET 4	
			Weight	Reps	Weight	Reps	Weight	Reps	Weight	Reps

WEDNESDAY	Focus area	Equipment	SET 1		SET 2		SET 3		SET 4	
			Weight	Reps	Weight	Reps	Weight	Reps	Weight	Reps

THURSDAY	Focus area	Equipment	SET 1		SET 2		SET 3		SET 4	
			Weight	Reps	Weight	Reps	Weight	Reps	Weight	Reps

FRIDAY	Focus area	Equipment	SET 1		SET 2		SET 3		SET 4	
			Weight	Reps	Weight	Reps	Weight	Reps	Weight	Reps

SATURDAY	Focus area	Equipment	SET 1		SET 2		SET 3		SET 4	
			Weight	Reps	Weight	Reps	Weight	Reps	Weight	Reps

SUNDAY	Focus area	Equipment	SET 1		SET 2		SET 3		SET 4	
			Weight	Reps	Weight	Reps	Weight	Reps	Weight	Reps

Cardio Training

MONDAY

Exercise	Time	Distance/ resistance	Intensity	Heart rate	Ease	Cal/kJ expended
						Total:

TUESDAY

Exercise	Time	Distance/ resistance	Intensity	Heart rate	Ease	Cal/kJ expended
						Total:

WEDNESDAY

Exercise	Time	Distance/ resistance	Intensity	Heart rate	Ease	Cal/kJ expended
						Total:

THURSDAY

Exercise	Time	Distance/ resistance	Intensity	Heart rate	Ease	Cal/kJ expended
						Total:

FRIDAY

Exercise	Time	Distance/ resistance	Intensity	Heart rate	Ease	Cal/kJ expended
						Total:

SATURDAY

Exercise	Time	Distance/ resistance	Intensity	Heart rate	Ease	Cal/kJ expended
						Total:

SUNDAY

Exercise	Time	Distance/ resistance	Intensity	Heart rate	Ease	Cal/kJ expended
						Total:
						Weekly Total:

Food Diary

MONDAY		Cal/kJ	Fat	Protein	Carbs
Breakfast time: am/pm					
Lunch time: am/pm					
Dinner time: am/pm					
Snacks:					
Coffees/teas:	Fluid intake: **Totals:**				

TUESDAY		Cal/kJ	Fat	Protein	Carbs
Breakfast time: am/pm					
Lunch time: am/pm					
Dinner time: am/pm					
Snacks:					
Coffees/teas:	Fluid intake: **Totals:**				

WEDNESDAY		Cal/kJ	Fat	Protein	Carbs
Breakfast time: am/pm					
Lunch time: am/pm					
Dinner time: am/pm					
Snacks:					
Coffees/teas:	Fluid intake: **Totals:**				

THURSDAY		Cal/kJ	Fat	Protein	Carbs
Breakfast time: am/pm					
Lunch time: am/pm					
Dinner time: am/pm					
Snacks:					
Coffees/teas:	Fluid intake: **Totals:**				

FRIDAY		Cal/kJ	Fat	Protein	Carbs
Breakfast time: am/pm					
Lunch time: am/pm					
Dinner time: am/pm					
Snacks:					
Coffees/teas:	Fluid intake: **Totals:**				

SATURDAY		Cal/kJ	Fat	Protein	Carbs
Breakfast time: am/pm					
Lunch time: am/pm					
Dinner time: am/pm					
Snacks:					
Coffees/teas:	Fluid intake: **Totals:**				

SUNDAY		Cal/kJ	Fat	Protein	Carbs
Breakfast time: am/pm					
Lunch time: am/pm					
Dinner time: am/pm					
Snacks:					
Coffees/teas:	Fluid intake: **Totals:**				

Units of alcohol this week: Total alcohol Cal/kJ:

Vitamins and supplements

Weekly Totals	Cal/kJ	Fat	Protein	Carbs

Weekly Personal Summary

Energy level 1–5

Stress level 1–5

Hours of sleep

Sleep quality 1–5

Mood 1–5

Appetite 1–5

Cal/kJ intake

Planned Cal/kJ	
Actual Cal/kJ	

Difference [+/-]

Weight at start of week

Weight at end of week

BMI at start of week

BMI at end of week

Injuries or illnesses

Week Beginning

/ /

Planned exercise sessions this week

	Exercise	Completed [Y/N]
Monday		
Tuesday		
Wednesday		
Thursday		
Friday		
Saturday		
Sunday		

Strength Training

MONDAY	Focus area	Equipment	SET 1		SET 2		SET 3		SET 4	
			Weight	Reps	Weight	Reps	Weight	Reps	Weight	Reps

TUESDAY	Focus area	Equipment	SET 1		SET 2		SET 3		SET 4	
			Weight	Reps	Weight	Reps	Weight	Reps	Weight	Reps

WEDNESDAY	Focus area	Equipment	SET 1		SET 2		SET 3		SET 4	
			Weight	Reps	Weight	Reps	Weight	Reps	Weight	Reps

THURSDAY	Focus area	Equipment	SET 1		SET 2		SET 3		SET 4	
			Weight	Reps	Weight	Reps	Weight	Reps	Weight	Reps

FRIDAY	Focus area	Equipment	SET 1		SET 2		SET 3		SET 4	
			Weight	Reps	Weight	Reps	Weight	Reps	Weight	Reps

SATURDAY	Focus area	Equipment	SET 1		SET 2		SET 3		SET 4	
			Weight	Reps	Weight	Reps	Weight	Reps	Weight	Reps

SUNDAY	Focus area	Equipment	SET 1		SET 2		SET 3		SET 4	
			Weight	Reps	Weight	Reps	Weight	Reps	Weight	Reps

Cardio Training

MONDAY

Exercise	Time	Distance/ resistance	Intensity	Heart rate	Ease	Cal/kJ expended
						Total:

TUESDAY

Exercise	Time	Distance/ resistance	Intensity	Heart rate	Ease	Cal/kJ expended
						Total:

WEDNESDAY

Exercise	Time	Distance/ resistance	Intensity	Heart rate	Ease	Cal/kJ expended
						Total:

THURSDAY

Exercise	Time	Distance/ resistance	Intensity	Heart rate	Ease	Cal/kJ expended
						Total:

FRIDAY

Exercise	Time	Distance/ resistance	Intensity	Heart rate	Ease	Cal/kJ expended
						Total:

SATURDAY

Exercise	Time	Distance/ resistance	Intensity	Heart rate	Ease	Cal/kJ expended
						Total:

SUNDAY

Exercise	Time	Distance/ resistance	Intensity	Heart rate	Ease	Cal/kJ expended
						Total:

Weekly Total:

Food Diary

MONDAY			Cal/kJ	Fat	Protein	Carbs
Breakfast time: am/pm						
Lunch time: am/pm						
Dinner time: am/pm						
Snacks:						
Coffees/teas:	Fluid intake:	**Totals:**				

TUESDAY			Cal/kJ	Fat	Protein	Carbs
Breakfast time: am/pm						
Lunch time: am/pm						
Dinner time: am/pm						
Snacks:						
Coffees/teas:	Fluid intake:	**Totals:**				

WEDNESDAY			Cal/kJ	Fat	Protein	Carbs
Breakfast time: am/pm						
Lunch time: am/pm						
Dinner time: am/pm						
Snacks:						
Coffees/teas:	Fluid intake:	**Totals:**				

THURSDAY			Cal/kJ	Fat	Protein	Carbs
Breakfast time: am/pm						
Lunch time: am/pm						
Dinner time: am/pm						
Snacks:						
Coffees/teas:	Fluid intake:	**Totals:**				

FRIDAY		Cal/kJ	Fat	Protein	Carbs
Breakfast time: am/pm					
Lunch time: am/pm					
Dinner time: am/pm					
Snacks:					
Coffees/teas:	Fluid intake: **Totals:**				

SATURDAY		Cal/kJ	Fat	Protein	Carbs
Breakfast time: am/pm					
Lunch time: am/pm					
Dinner time: am/pm					
Snacks:					
Coffees/teas:	Fluid intake: **Totals:**				

SUNDAY		Cal/kJ	Fat	Protein	Carbs
Breakfast time: am/pm					
Lunch time: am/pm					
Dinner time: am/pm					
Snacks:					
Coffees/teas:	Fluid intake: **Totals:**				

Units of alcohol this week: Total alcohol Cal/kJ:

Vitamins and supplements

Weekly Totals	Cal/kJ	Fat	Protein	Carbs

Weekly Personal Summary

Energy level 1–5 Stress level 1–5

Hours of sleep Sleep quality 1–5

Mood 1–5 Appetite 1–5

Cal/kJ intake

Planned Cal/kJ	
Actual Cal/kJ	
Difference [+/-]	

Weight at start of week

Weight at end of week

BMI at start of week

BMI at end of week

Injuries or illnesses

Week Beginning

/ /

Planned exercise sessions this week

	Exercise	Completed [Y/N]
Monday		
Tuesday		
Wednesday		
Thursday		
Friday		
Saturday		
Sunday		

Strength Training

	Focus area	Equipment	SET 1		SET 2		SET 3		SET 4	
			Weight	Reps	Weight	Reps	Weight	Reps	Weight	Reps
MONDAY										

	Focus area	Equipment	SET 1		SET 2		SET 3		SET 4	
			Weight	Reps	Weight	Reps	Weight	Reps	Weight	Reps
TUESDAY										

	Focus area	Equipment	SET 1		SET 2		SET 3		SET 4	
			Weight	Reps	Weight	Reps	Weight	Reps	Weight	Reps
WEDNESDAY										

	Focus area	Equipment	SET 1		SET 2		SET 3		SET 4	
			Weight	Reps	Weight	Reps	Weight	Reps	Weight	Reps
THURSDAY										

	Focus area	Equipment	SET 1		SET 2		SET 3		SET 4	
			Weight	Reps	Weight	Reps	Weight	Reps	Weight	Reps
FRIDAY										

	Focus area	Equipment	SET 1		SET 2		SET 3		SET 4	
			Weight	Reps	Weight	Reps	Weight	Reps	Weight	Reps
SATURDAY										

	Focus area	Equipment	SET 1		SET 2		SET 3		SET 4	
			Weight	Reps	Weight	Reps	Weight	Reps	Weight	Reps
SUNDAY										

Cardio Training

MONDAY	Exercise	Time	Distance/ resistance	Intensity	Heart rate	Ease	Cal/kJ expended
							Total:

TUESDAY	Exercise	Time	Distance/ resistance	Intensity	Heart rate	Ease	Cal/kJ expended
							Total:

WEDNESDAY	Exercise	Time	Distance/ resistance	Intensity	Heart rate	Ease	Cal/kJ expended
							Total:

THURSDAY	Exercise	Time	Distance/ resistance	Intensity	Heart rate	Ease	Cal/kJ expended
							Total:

FRIDAY	Exercise	Time	Distance/ resistance	Intensity	Heart rate	Ease	Cal/kJ expended
							Total:

SATURDAY	Exercise	Time	Distance/ resistance	Intensity	Heart rate	Ease	Cal/kJ expended
							Total:

SUNDAY	Exercise	Time	Distance/ resistance	Intensity	Heart rate	Ease	Cal/kJ expended
							Total:
							Weekly Total:

Food Diary

MONDAY		Cal/kJ	Fat	Protein	Carbs
Breakfast time: am/pm					
Lunch time: am/pm					
Dinner time: am/pm					
Snacks:					
Coffees/teas:	Fluid intake: **Totals:**				

TUESDAY		Cal/kJ	Fat	Protein	Carbs
Breakfast time: am/pm					
Lunch time: am/pm					
Dinner time: am/pm					
Snacks:					
Coffees/teas:	Fluid intake: **Totals:**				

WEDNESDAY		Cal/kJ	Fat	Protein	Carbs
Breakfast time: am/pm					
Lunch time: am/pm					
Dinner time: am/pm					
Snacks:					
Coffees/teas:	Fluid intake: **Totals:**				

THURSDAY		Cal/kJ	Fat	Protein	Carbs
Breakfast time: am/pm					
Lunch time: am/pm					
Dinner time: am/pm					
Snacks:					
Coffees/teas:	Fluid intake: **Totals:**				

FRIDAY		Cal/kJ	Fat	Protein	Carbs
Breakfast time: am/pm					
Lunch time: am/pm					
Dinner time: am/pm					
Snacks:					
Coffees/teas:	Fluid intake: **Totals:**				

SATURDAY		Cal/kJ	Fat	Protein	Carbs
Breakfast time: am/pm					
Lunch time: am/pm					
Dinner time: am/pm					
Snacks:					
Coffees/teas:	Fluid intake: **Totals:**				

SUNDAY		Cal/kJ	Fat	Protein	Carbs
Breakfast time: am/pm					
Lunch time: am/pm					
Dinner time: am/pm					
Snacks:					
Coffees/teas:	Fluid intake: **Totals:**				

Units of alcohol this week: Total alcohol Cal/kJ:

Vitamins and supplements

Weekly Totals	Cal/kJ	Fat	Protein	Carbs

Weekly Personal Summary

Energy level 1–5

Stress level 1–5

Hours of sleep

Sleep quality 1–5

Mood 1–5

Appetite 1–5

Cal/kJ intake

Planned Cal/kJ	
Actual Cal/kJ	

Difference [+/-]

Weight at start of week

Weight at end of week

BMI at start of week

BMI at end of week

Injuries or illnesses

Week Beginning

/ /

Planned exercise sessions this week

	Exercise	Completed [Y/N]
Monday		
Tuesday		
Wednesday		
Thursday		
Friday		
Saturday		
Sunday		

Strength Training

MONDAY

Focus area	Equipment	SET 1		SET 2		SET 3		SET 4	
		Weight	Reps	Weight	Reps	Weight	Reps	Weight	Reps

TUESDAY

Focus area	Equipment	SET 1		SET 2		SET 3		SET 4	
		Weight	Reps	Weight	Reps	Weight	Reps	Weight	Reps

WEDNESDAY

Focus area	Equipment	SET 1		SET 2		SET 3		SET 4	
		Weight	Reps	Weight	Reps	Weight	Reps	Weight	Reps

THURSDAY

Focus area	Equipment	SET 1		SET 2		SET 3		SET 4	
		Weight	Reps	Weight	Reps	Weight	Reps	Weight	Reps

FRIDAY

Focus area	Equipment	SET 1		SET 2		SET 3		SET 4	
		Weight	Reps	Weight	Reps	Weight	Reps	Weight	Reps

SATURDAY

Focus area	Equipment	SET 1		SET 2		SET 3		SET 4	
		Weight	Reps	Weight	Reps	Weight	Reps	Weight	Reps

SUNDAY

Focus area	Equipment	SET 1		SET 2		SET 3		SET 4	
		Weight	Reps	Weight	Reps	Weight	Reps	Weight	Reps

Cardio Training

MONDAY

Exercise	Time	Distance/ resistance	Intensity	Heart rate	Ease	Cal/kJ expended
						Total:

TUESDAY

Exercise	Time	Distance/ resistance	Intensity	Heart rate	Ease	Cal/kJ expended
						Total:

WEDNESDAY

Exercise	Time	Distance/ resistance	Intensity	Heart rate	Ease	Cal/kJ expended
						Total:

THURSDAY

Exercise	Time	Distance/ resistance	Intensity	Heart rate	Ease	Cal/kJ expended
						Total:

FRIDAY

Exercise	Time	Distance/ resistance	Intensity	Heart rate	Ease	Cal/kJ expended
						Total:

SATURDAY

Exercise	Time	Distance/ resistance	Intensity	Heart rate	Ease	Cal/kJ expended
						Total:

SUNDAY

Exercise	Time	Distance/ resistance	Intensity	Heart rate	Ease	Cal/kJ expended
						Total:
						Weekly Total:

Food Diary

MONDAY			Cal/kJ	Fat	Protein	Carbs
Breakfast time: am/pm						
Lunch time: am/pm						
Dinner time: am/pm						
Snacks:						
Coffees/teas:	Fluid intake:	**Totals:**				

TUESDAY			Cal/kJ	Fat	Protein	Carbs
Breakfast time: am/pm						
Lunch time: am/pm						
Dinner time: am/pm						
Snacks:						
Coffees/teas:	Fluid intake:	**Totals:**				

WEDNESDAY			Cal/kJ	Fat	Protein	Carbs
Breakfast time: am/pm						
Lunch time: am/pm						
Dinner time: am/pm						
Snacks:						
Coffees/teas:	Fluid intake:	**Totals:**				

THURSDAY			Cal/kJ	Fat	Protein	Carbs
Breakfast time: am/pm						
Lunch time: am/pm						
Dinner time: am/pm						
Snacks:						
Coffees/teas:	Fluid intake:	**Totals:**				

FRIDAY		Cal/kJ	Fat	Protein	Carbs
Breakfast time: am/pm					
Lunch time: am/pm					
Dinner time: am/pm					
Snacks:					
Coffees/teas:	Fluid intake: **Totals:**				

SATURDAY		Cal/kJ	Fat	Protein	Carbs
Breakfast time: am/pm					
Lunch time: am/pm					
Dinner time: am/pm					
Snacks:					
Coffees/teas:	Fluid intake: **Totals:**				

SUNDAY		Cal/kJ	Fat	Protein	Carbs
Breakfast time: am/pm					
Lunch time: am/pm					
Dinner time: am/pm					
Snacks:					
Coffees/teas:	Fluid intake: **Totals:**				

Units of alcohol this week: Total alcohol Cal/kJ:

Vitamins and supplements

Weekly Totals	Cal/kJ	Fat	Protein	Carbs

Weekly Personal Summary

Energy level (1–5)

Stress level (1–5)

Hours of sleep

Sleep quality (1–5)

Mood (1–5)

Appetite (1–5)

Cal/kJ intake

Planned Cal/kJ	
Actual Cal/kJ	
Difference [+/-]	

Weight at start of week

Weight at end of week

BMI at start of week

BMI at end of week

Injuries or illnesses

Week Beginning

/ /

Planned exercise sessions this week

	Exercise	Completed [Y/N]
Monday		
Tuesday		
Wednesday		
Thursday		
Friday		
Saturday		
Sunday		

Strength Training

MONDAY

Focus area	Equipment	SET 1		SET 2		SET 3		SET 4	
		Weight	Reps	Weight	Reps	Weight	Reps	Weight	Reps

TUESDAY

Focus area	Equipment	SET 1		SET 2		SET 3		SET 4	
		Weight	Reps	Weight	Reps	Weight	Reps	Weight	Reps

WEDNESDAY

Focus area	Equipment	SET 1		SET 2		SET 3		SET 4	
		Weight	Reps	Weight	Reps	Weight	Reps	Weight	Reps

THURSDAY

Focus area	Equipment	SET 1		SET 2		SET 3		SET 4	
		Weight	Reps	Weight	Reps	Weight	Reps	Weight	Reps

FRIDAY

Focus area	Equipment	SET 1		SET 2		SET 3		SET 4	
		Weight	Reps	Weight	Reps	Weight	Reps	Weight	Reps

SATURDAY

Focus area	Equipment	SET 1		SET 2		SET 3		SET 4	
		Weight	Reps	Weight	Reps	Weight	Reps	Weight	Reps

SUNDAY

Focus area	Equipment	SET 1		SET 2		SET 3		SET 4	
		Weight	Reps	Weight	Reps	Weight	Reps	Weight	Reps

Cardio Training

MONDAY

Exercise	Time	Distance/ resistance	Intensity	Heart rate	Ease	Cal/kJ expended

Total:

TUESDAY

Exercise	Time	Distance/ resistance	Intensity	Heart rate	Ease	Cal/kJ expended

Total:

WEDNESDAY

Exercise	Time	Distance/ resistance	Intensity	Heart rate	Ease	Cal/kJ expended

Total:

THURSDAY

Exercise	Time	Distance/ resistance	Intensity	Heart rate	Ease	Cal/kJ expended

Total:

FRIDAY

Exercise	Time	Distance/ resistance	Intensity	Heart rate	Ease	Cal/kJ expended

Total:

SATURDAY

Exercise	Time	Distance/ resistance	Intensity	Heart rate	Ease	Cal/kJ expended

Total:

SUNDAY

Exercise	Time	Distance/ resistance	Intensity	Heart rate	Ease	Cal/kJ expended

Total:

Weekly Total:

Food Diary

MONDAY		Cal/kJ	Fat	Protein	Carbs
Breakfast time: am/pm					
Lunch time: am/pm					
Dinner time: am/pm					
Snacks:					
Coffees/teas:	Fluid intake: **Totals:**				

TUESDAY		Cal/kJ	Fat	Protein	Carbs
Breakfast time: am/pm					
Lunch time: am/pm					
Dinner time: am/pm					
Snacks:					
Coffees/teas:	Fluid intake: **Totals:**				

WEDNESDAY		Cal/kJ	Fat	Protein	Carbs
Breakfast time: am/pm					
Lunch time: am/pm					
Dinner time: am/pm					
Snacks:					
Coffees/teas:	Fluid intake: **Totals:**				

THURSDAY		Cal/kJ	Fat	Protein	Carbs
Breakfast time: am/pm					
Lunch time: am/pm					
Dinner time: am/pm					
Snacks:					
Coffees/teas:	Fluid intake: **Totals:**				

FRIDAY		Cal/kJ	Fat	Protein	Carbs
Breakfast time: am/pm					
Lunch time: am/pm					
Dinner time: am/pm					
Snacks:					
Coffees/teas: Fluid intake:	**Totals:**				

SATURDAY		Cal/kJ	Fat	Protein	Carbs
Breakfast time: am/pm					
Lunch time: am/pm					
Dinner time: am/pm					
Snacks:					
Coffees/teas: Fluid intake:	**Totals:**				

SUNDAY		Cal/kJ	Fat	Protein	Carbs
Breakfast time: am/pm					
Lunch time: am/pm					
Dinner time: am/pm					
Snacks:					
Coffees/teas: Fluid intake:	**Totals:**				

Units of alcohol this week: Total alcohol Cal/kJ:

Vitamins and supplements

Weekly Totals	Cal/kJ	Fat	Protein	Carbs

Weekly Personal Summary

Energy level (1–5) Stress level (1–5)

Hours of sleep Sleep quality (1–5)

Mood (1–5) Appetite (1–5)

Cal/kJ intake

Planned Cal/kJ	
Actual Cal/kJ	

Difference [+/-]

Weight at start of week

Weight at end of week

BMI at start of week

BMI at end of week

Injuries or illnesses

Week Beginning

/ /

Planned exercise sessions this week

	Exercise	Completed [Y/N]
Monday		
Tuesday		
Wednesday		
Thursday		
Friday		
Saturday		
Sunday		

Strength Training

	Focus area	Equipment	SET 1		SET 2		SET 3		SET 4	
			Weight	Reps	Weight	Reps	Weight	Reps	Weight	Reps
MONDAY										

	Focus area	Equipment	SET 1		SET 2		SET 3		SET 4	
			Weight	Reps	Weight	Reps	Weight	Reps	Weight	Reps
TUESDAY										

	Focus area	Equipment	SET 1		SET 2		SET 3		SET 4	
			Weight	Reps	Weight	Reps	Weight	Reps	Weight	Reps
WEDNESDAY										

	Focus area	Equipment	SET 1		SET 2		SET 3		SET 4	
			Weight	Reps	Weight	Reps	Weight	Reps	Weight	Reps
THURSDAY										

	Focus area	Equipment	SET 1		SET 2		SET 3		SET 4	
			Weight	Reps	Weight	Reps	Weight	Reps	Weight	Reps
FRIDAY										

	Focus area	Equipment	SET 1		SET 2		SET 3		SET 4	
			Weight	Reps	Weight	Reps	Weight	Reps	Weight	Reps
SATURDAY										

	Focus area	Equipment	SET 1		SET 2		SET 3		SET 4	
			Weight	Reps	Weight	Reps	Weight	Reps	Weight	Reps
SUNDAY										

Cardio Training

MONDAY	Exercise	Time	Distance/ resistance	Intensity	Heart rate	Ease	Cal/kJ expended
							Total:

TUESDAY	Exercise	Time	Distance/ resistance	Intensity	Heart rate	Ease	Cal/kJ expended
							Total:

WEDNESDAY	Exercise	Time	Distance/ resistance	Intensity	Heart rate	Ease	Cal/kJ expended
							Total:

THURSDAY	Exercise	Time	Distance/ resistance	Intensity	Heart rate	Ease	Cal/kJ expended
							Total:

FRIDAY	Exercise	Time	Distance/ resistance	Intensity	Heart rate	Ease	Cal/kJ expended
							Total:

SATURDAY	Exercise	Time	Distance/ resistance	Intensity	Heart rate	Ease	Cal/kJ expended
							Total:

SUNDAY	Exercise	Time	Distance/ resistance	Intensity	Heart rate	Ease	Cal/kJ expended
							Total:
							Weekly Total:

Food Diary

MONDAY		Cal/kJ	Fat	Protein	Carbs
Breakfast time: am/pm					
Lunch time: am/pm					
Dinner time: am/pm					
Snacks:					
Coffees/teas:	Fluid intake: **Totals:**				

TUESDAY		Cal/kJ	Fat	Protein	Carbs
Breakfast time: am/pm					
Lunch time: am/pm					
Dinner time: am/pm					
Snacks:					
Coffees/teas:	Fluid intake: **Totals:**				

WEDNESDAY		Cal/kJ	Fat	Protein	Carbs
Breakfast time: am/pm					
Lunch time: am/pm					
Dinner time: am/pm					
Snacks:					
Coffees/teas:	Fluid intake: **Totals:**				

THURSDAY		Cal/kJ	Fat	Protein	Carbs
Breakfast time: am/pm					
Lunch time: am/pm					
Dinner time: am/pm					
Snacks:					
Coffees/teas:	Fluid intake: **Totals:**				

FRIDAY		Cal/kJ	Fat	Protein	Carbs
Breakfast time: am/pm					
Lunch time: am/pm					
Dinner time: am/pm					
Snacks:					
Coffees/teas:	Fluid intake: **Totals:**				

SATURDAY		Cal/kJ	Fat	Protein	Carbs
Breakfast time: am/pm					
Lunch time: am/pm					
Dinner time: am/pm					
Snacks:					
Coffees/teas:	Fluid intake: **Totals:**				

SUNDAY		Cal/kJ	Fat	Protein	Carbs
Breakfast time: am/pm					
Lunch time: am/pm					
Dinner time: am/pm					
Snacks:					
Coffees/teas:	Fluid intake: **Totals:**				

Units of alcohol this week: Total alcohol Cal/kJ:

Vitamins and supplements

Weekly Totals	Cal/kJ	Fat	Protein	Carbs

Weekly Personal Summary

Energy level (1–5) Stress level (1–5)

Hours of sleep Sleep quality (1–5)

Mood (1–5) Appetite (1–5)

Cal/kJ intake

Planned Cal/kJ

Actual Cal/kJ

Difference [+/-]

Weight at start of week

Weight at end of week

BMI at start of week

BMI at end of week

Injuries or illnesses

Week Beginning

/ /

Strength Training

Planned exercise sessions this week

	Exercise	Completed [Y/N]
Monday		
Tuesday		
Wednesday		
Thursday		
Friday		
Saturday		
Sunday		

MONDAY

Focus area	Equipment	SET 1		SET 2		SET 3		SET 4	
		Weight	Reps	Weight	Reps	Weight	Reps	Weight	Reps

TUESDAY

Focus area	Equipment	SET 1		SET 2		SET 3		SET 4	
		Weight	Reps	Weight	Reps	Weight	Reps	Weight	Reps

WEDNESDAY

Focus area	Equipment	SET 1		SET 2		SET 3		SET 4	
		Weight	Reps	Weight	Reps	Weight	Reps	Weight	Reps

THURSDAY

Focus area	Equipment	SET 1		SET 2		SET 3		SET 4	
		Weight	Reps	Weight	Reps	Weight	Reps	Weight	Reps

FRIDAY

Focus area	Equipment	SET 1		SET 2		SET 3		SET 4	
		Weight	Reps	Weight	Reps	Weight	Reps	Weight	Reps

SATURDAY

Focus area	Equipment	SET 1		SET 2		SET 3		SET 4	
		Weight	Reps	Weight	Reps	Weight	Reps	Weight	Reps

SUNDAY

Focus area	Equipment	SET 1		SET 2		SET 3		SET 4	
		Weight	Reps	Weight	Reps	Weight	Reps	Weight	Reps

Cardio Training

MONDAY

Exercise	Time	Distance/ resistance	Intensity	Heart rate	Ease	Cal/kJ expended
						Total:

TUESDAY

Exercise	Time	Distance/ resistance	Intensity	Heart rate	Ease	Cal/kJ expended
						Total:

WEDNESDAY

Exercise	Time	Distance/ resistance	Intensity	Heart rate	Ease	Cal/kJ expended
						Total:

THURSDAY

Exercise	Time	Distance/ resistance	Intensity	Heart rate	Ease	Cal/kJ expended
						Total:

FRIDAY

Exercise	Time	Distance/ resistance	Intensity	Heart rate	Ease	Cal/kJ expended
						Total:

SATURDAY

Exercise	Time	Distance/ resistance	Intensity	Heart rate	Ease	Cal/kJ expended
						Total:

SUNDAY

Exercise	Time	Distance/ resistance	Intensity	Heart rate	Ease	Cal/kJ expended
						Total:
					Weekly Total:	

Food Diary

MONDAY		Cal/kJ	Fat	Protein	Carbs
Breakfast time: am/pm					
Lunch time: am/pm					
Dinner time: am/pm					
Snacks:					
Coffees/teas:	Fluid intake: **Totals:**				

TUESDAY		Cal/kJ	Fat	Protein	Carbs
Breakfast time: am/pm					
Lunch time: am/pm					
Dinner time: am/pm					
Snacks:					
Coffees/teas:	Fluid intake: **Totals:**				

WEDNESDAY		Cal/kJ	Fat	Protein	Carbs
Breakfast time: am/pm					
Lunch time: am/pm					
Dinner time: am/pm					
Snacks:					
Coffees/teas:	Fluid intake: **Totals:**				

THURSDAY		Cal/kJ	Fat	Protein	Carbs
Breakfast time: am/pm					
Lunch time: am/pm					
Dinner time: am/pm					
Snacks:					
Coffees/teas:	Fluid intake: **Totals:**				

FRIDAY		Cal/kJ	Fat	Protein	Carbs
Breakfast time: am/pm					
Lunch time: am/pm					
Dinner time: am/pm					
Snacks:					
Coffees/teas:	Fluid intake: **Totals:**				

SATURDAY		Cal/kJ	Fat	Protein	Carbs
Breakfast time: am/pm					
Lunch time: am/pm					
Dinner time: am/pm					
Snacks:					
Coffees/teas:	Fluid intake: **Totals:**				

SUNDAY		Cal/kJ	Fat	Protein	Carbs
Breakfast time: am/pm					
Lunch time: am/pm					
Dinner time: am/pm					
Snacks:					
Coffees/teas:	Fluid intake: **Totals:**				

Units of alcohol this week: Total alcohol Cal/kJ:

Vitamins and supplements

Weekly Totals	Cal/kJ	Fat	Protein	Carbs

Weekly Personal Summary

Energy level 1–5

Stress level 1–5

Hours of sleep

Sleep quality 1–5

Mood 1–5

Appetite 1–5

Cal/kJ intake

Planned Cal/kJ	
Actual Cal/kJ	

Difference [+/-]

Weight at start of week

Weight at end of week

BMI at start of week

BMI at end of week

Injuries or illnesses

Week Beginning

/ /

Strength Training

Planned exercise sessions this week

	Exercise	Completed [Y/N]
Monday		
Tuesday		
Wednesday		
Thursday		
Friday		
Saturday		
Sunday		

MONDAY	Focus area	Equipment	SET 1		SET 2		SET 3		SET 4	
			Weight	Reps	Weight	Reps	Weight	Reps	Weight	Reps

TUESDAY	Focus area	Equipment	SET 1		SET 2		SET 3		SET 4	
			Weight	Reps	Weight	Reps	Weight	Reps	Weight	Reps

WEDNESDAY	Focus area	Equipment	SET 1		SET 2		SET 3		SET 4	
			Weight	Reps	Weight	Reps	Weight	Reps	Weight	Reps

THURSDAY	Focus area	Equipment	SET 1		SET 2		SET 3		SET 4	
			Weight	Reps	Weight	Reps	Weight	Reps	Weight	Reps

FRIDAY	Focus area	Equipment	SET 1		SET 2		SET 3		SET 4	
			Weight	Reps	Weight	Reps	Weight	Reps	Weight	Reps

SATURDAY	Focus area	Equipment	SET 1		SET 2		SET 3		SET 4	
			Weight	Reps	Weight	Reps	Weight	Reps	Weight	Reps

SUNDAY	Focus area	Equipment	SET 1		SET 2		SET 3		SET 4	
			Weight	Reps	Weight	Reps	Weight	Reps	Weight	Reps

Cardio Training

MONDAY

Exercise	Time	Distance/ resistance	Intensity	Heart rate	Ease	Cal/kJ expended
						Total:

TUESDAY

Exercise	Time	Distance/ resistance	Intensity	Heart rate	Ease	Cal/kJ expended
						Total:

WEDNESDAY

Exercise	Time	Distance/ resistance	Intensity	Heart rate	Ease	Cal/kJ expended
						Total:

THURSDAY

Exercise	Time	Distance/ resistance	Intensity	Heart rate	Ease	Cal/kJ expended
						Total:

FRIDAY

Exercise	Time	Distance/ resistance	Intensity	Heart rate	Ease	Cal/kJ expended
						Total:

SATURDAY

Exercise	Time	Distance/ resistance	Intensity	Heart rate	Ease	Cal/kJ expended
						Total:

SUNDAY

Exercise	Time	Distance/ resistance	Intensity	Heart rate	Ease	Cal/kJ expended
						Total:
						Weekly Total:

Food Diary

MONDAY			Cal/kJ	Fat	Protein	Carbs
Breakfast time: am/pm						
Lunch time: am/pm						
Dinner time: am/pm						
Snacks:						
Coffees/teas:	Fluid intake:	**Totals:**				

TUESDAY			Cal/kJ	Fat	Protein	Carbs
Breakfast time: am/pm						
Lunch time: am/pm						
Dinner time: am/pm						
Snacks:						
Coffees/teas:	Fluid intake:	**Totals:**				

WEDNESDAY			Cal/kJ	Fat	Protein	Carbs
Breakfast time: am/pm						
Lunch time: am/pm						
Dinner time: am/pm						
Snacks:						
Coffees/teas:	Fluid intake:	**Totals:**				

THURSDAY			Cal/kJ	Fat	Protein	Carbs
Breakfast time: am/pm						
Lunch time: am/pm						
Dinner time: am/pm						
Snacks:						
Coffees/teas:	Fluid intake:	**Totals:**				

FRIDAY		Cal/kJ	Fat	Protein	Carbs
Breakfast time: am/pm					
Lunch time: am/pm					
Dinner time: am/pm					
Snacks:					
Coffees/teas:	Fluid intake: **Totals:**				

SATURDAY		Cal/kJ	Fat	Protein	Carbs
Breakfast time: am/pm					
Lunch time: am/pm					
Dinner time: am/pm					
Snacks:					
Coffees/teas:	Fluid intake: **Totals:**				

SUNDAY		Cal/kJ	Fat	Protein	Carbs
Breakfast time: am/pm					
Lunch time: am/pm					
Dinner time: am/pm					
Snacks:					
Coffees/teas:	Fluid intake: **Totals:**				

Units of alcohol this week: Total alcohol Cal/kJ:

Vitamins and supplements

Weekly Totals	Cal/kJ	Fat	Protein	Carbs

Weekly Personal Summary

Energy level 1–5

Stress level 1–5

Hours of sleep

Sleep quality 1–5

Mood 1–5

Appetite 1–5

Cal/kJ intake

Planned Cal/kJ	
Actual Cal/kJ	

Difference [+/-]

Weight at start of week

Weight at end of week

BMI at start of week

BMI at end of week

Injuries or illnesses

Week Beginning

/ /

Planned exercise sessions this week

	Exercise	Completed [Y/N]
Monday		
Tuesday		
Wednesday		
Thursday		
Friday		
Saturday		
Sunday		

Strength Training

	Focus area	Equipment	SET 1		SET 2		SET 3		SET 4	
			Weight	Reps	Weight	Reps	Weight	Reps	Weight	Reps
MONDAY										

	Focus area	Equipment	SET 1		SET 2		SET 3		SET 4	
			Weight	Reps	Weight	Reps	Weight	Reps	Weight	Reps
TUESDAY										

	Focus area	Equipment	SET 1		SET 2		SET 3		SET 4	
			Weight	Reps	Weight	Reps	Weight	Reps	Weight	Reps
WEDNESDAY										

	Focus area	Equipment	SET 1		SET 2		SET 3		SET 4	
			Weight	Reps	Weight	Reps	Weight	Reps	Weight	Reps
THURSDAY										

	Focus area	Equipment	SET 1		SET 2		SET 3		SET 4	
			Weight	Reps	Weight	Reps	Weight	Reps	Weight	Reps
FRIDAY										

	Focus area	Equipment	SET 1		SET 2		SET 3		SET 4	
			Weight	Reps	Weight	Reps	Weight	Reps	Weight	Reps
SATURDAY										

	Focus area	Equipment	SET 1		SET 2		SET 3		SET 4	
			Weight	Reps	Weight	Reps	Weight	Reps	Weight	Reps
SUNDAY										

Cardio Training

MONDAY	Exercise	Time	Distance/ resistance	Intensity	Heart rate	Ease	Cal/kJ expended
							Total:

TUESDAY	Exercise	Time	Distance/ resistance	Intensity	Heart rate	Ease	Cal/kJ expended
							Total:

WEDNESDAY	Exercise	Time	Distance/ resistance	Intensity	Heart rate	Ease	Cal/kJ expended
							Total:

THURSDAY	Exercise	Time	Distance/ resistance	Intensity	Heart rate	Ease	Cal/kJ expended
							Total:

FRIDAY	Exercise	Time	Distance/ resistance	Intensity	Heart rate	Ease	Cal/kJ expended
							Total:

SATURDAY	Exercise	Time	Distance/ resistance	Intensity	Heart rate	Ease	Cal/kJ expended
							Total:

SUNDAY	Exercise	Time	Distance/ resistance	Intensity	Heart rate	Ease	Cal/kJ expended
							Total:
							Weekly Total:

Food Diary

MONDAY		Cal/kJ	Fat	Protein	Carbs
Breakfast time: am/pm					
Lunch time: am/pm					
Dinner time: am/pm					
Snacks:					
Coffees/teas:	Fluid intake: **Totals:**				

TUESDAY		Cal/kJ	Fat	Protein	Carbs
Breakfast time: am/pm					
Lunch time: am/pm					
Dinner time: am/pm					
Snacks:					
Coffees/teas:	Fluid intake: **Totals:**				

WEDNESDAY		Cal/kJ	Fat	Protein	Carbs
Breakfast time: am/pm					
Lunch time: am/pm					
Dinner time: am/pm					
Snacks:					
Coffees/teas:	Fluid intake: **Totals:**				

THURSDAY		Cal/kJ	Fat	Protein	Carbs
Breakfast time: am/pm					
Lunch time: am/pm					
Dinner time: am/pm					
Snacks:					
Coffees/teas:	Fluid intake: **Totals:**				

FRIDAY		Cal/kJ	Fat	Protein	Carbs
Breakfast time: am/pm					
Lunch time: am/pm					
Dinner time: am/pm					
Snacks:					
Coffees/teas:	Fluid intake: **Totals:**				

SATURDAY		Cal/kJ	Fat	Protein	Carbs
Breakfast time: am/pm					
Lunch time: am/pm					
Dinner time: am/pm					
Snacks:					
Coffees/teas:	Fluid intake: **Totals:**				

SUNDAY		Cal/kJ	Fat	Protein	Carbs
Breakfast time: am/pm					
Lunch time: am/pm					
Dinner time: am/pm					
Snacks:					
Coffees/teas:	Fluid intake: **Totals:**				

Units of alcohol this week: Total alcohol Cal/kJ:

Vitamins and supplements

Weekly Totals	Cal/kJ	Fat	Protein	Carbs

Weekly Personal Summary

Energy level (1–5) Stress level (1–5)

Hours of sleep Sleep quality (1–5)

Mood (1–5) Appetite (1–5)

Cal/kJ intake

Planned Cal/kJ

Actual Cal/kJ

Difference [+/-]

Weight at start of week

Weight at end of week

BMI at start of week

BMI at end of week

Injuries or illnesses

Week Beginning

/ /

Strength Training

Planned exercise sessions this week

	Exercise	Completed [Y/N]
Monday		
Tuesday		
Wednesday		
Thursday		
Friday		
Saturday		
Sunday		

MONDAY	Focus area	Equipment	SET 1		SET 2		SET 3		SET 4	
			Weight	Reps	Weight	Reps	Weight	Reps	Weight	Reps

TUESDAY	Focus area	Equipment	SET 1		SET 2		SET 3		SET 4	
			Weight	Reps	Weight	Reps	Weight	Reps	Weight	Reps

WEDNESDAY	Focus area	Equipment	SET 1		SET 2		SET 3		SET 4	
			Weight	Reps	Weight	Reps	Weight	Reps	Weight	Reps

THURSDAY	Focus area	Equipment	SET 1		SET 2		SET 3		SET 4	
			Weight	Reps	Weight	Reps	Weight	Reps	Weight	Reps

FRIDAY	Focus area	Equipment	SET 1		SET 2		SET 3		SET 4	
			Weight	Reps	Weight	Reps	Weight	Reps	Weight	Reps

SATURDAY	Focus area	Equipment	SET 1		SET 2		SET 3		SET 4	
			Weight	Reps	Weight	Reps	Weight	Reps	Weight	Reps

SUNDAY	Focus area	Equipment	SET 1		SET 2		SET 3		SET 4	
			Weight	Reps	Weight	Reps	Weight	Reps	Weight	Reps

Cardio Training

MONDAY

Exercise	Time	Distance/ resistance	Intensity	Heart rate	Ease	Cal/kJ expended
						Total:

TUESDAY

Exercise	Time	Distance/ resistance	Intensity	Heart rate	Ease	Cal/kJ expended
						Total:

WEDNESDAY

Exercise	Time	Distance/ resistance	Intensity	Heart rate	Ease	Cal/kJ expended
						Total:

THURSDAY

Exercise	Time	Distance/ resistance	Intensity	Heart rate	Ease	Cal/kJ expended
						Total:

FRIDAY

Exercise	Time	Distance/ resistance	Intensity	Heart rate	Ease	Cal/kJ expended
						Total:

SATURDAY

Exercise	Time	Distance/ resistance	Intensity	Heart rate	Ease	Cal/kJ expended
						Total:

SUNDAY

Exercise	Time	Distance/ resistance	Intensity	Heart rate	Ease	Cal/kJ expended
						Total:
						Weekly Total:

Food Diary

MONDAY			Cal/kJ	Fat	Protein	Carbs
Breakfast time: am/pm						
Lunch time: am/pm						
Dinner time: am/pm						
Snacks:						
Coffees/teas:	Fluid intake:	**Totals:**				

TUESDAY			Cal/kJ	Fat	Protein	Carbs
Breakfast time: am/pm						
Lunch time: am/pm						
Dinner time: am/pm						
Snacks:						
Coffees/teas:	Fluid intake:	**Totals:**				

WEDNESDAY			Cal/kJ	Fat	Protein	Carbs
Breakfast time: am/pm						
Lunch time: am/pm						
Dinner time: am/pm						
Snacks:						
Coffees/teas:	Fluid intake:	**Totals:**				

THURSDAY			Cal/kJ	Fat	Protein	Carbs
Breakfast time: am/pm						
Lunch time: am/pm						
Dinner time: am/pm						
Snacks:						
Coffees/teas:	Fluid intake:	**Totals:**				

FRIDAY		Cal/kJ	Fat	Protein	Carbs
Breakfast time: am/pm					
Lunch time: am/pm					
Dinner time: am/pm					
Snacks:					
Coffees/teas:	Fluid intake: **Totals:**				

SATURDAY		Cal/kJ	Fat	Protein	Carbs
Breakfast time: am/pm					
Lunch time: am/pm					
Dinner time: am/pm					
Snacks:					
Coffees/teas:	Fluid intake: **Totals:**				

SUNDAY		Cal/kJ	Fat	Protein	Carbs
Breakfast time: am/pm					
Lunch time: am/pm					
Dinner time: am/pm					
Snacks:					
Coffees/teas:	Fluid intake: **Totals:**				

Units of alcohol this week: Total alcohol Cal/kJ:

Vitamins and supplements

Weekly Totals	Cal/kJ	Fat	Protein	Carbs

Weekly Personal Summary

Energy level (1–5)

Stress level (1–5)

Hours of sleep

Sleep quality (1–5)

Mood (1–5)

Appetite (1–5)

Cal/kJ intake

Planned Cal/kJ	
Actual Cal/kJ	

Difference [+/-]

Weight at start of week

Weight at end of week

BMI at start of week

BMI at end of week

Injuries or illnesses

Week Beginning

/ /

Planned exercise sessions this week

	Exercise	Completed [Y/N]
Monday		
Tuesday		
Wednesday		
Thursday		
Friday		
Saturday		
Sunday		

Strength Training

MONDAY	ocus area	Equipment	SET 1		SET 2		SET 3		SET 4	
			Weight	Reps	Weight	Reps	Weight	Reps	Weight	Reps

TUESDAY	ocus area	Equipment	SET 1		SET 2		SET 3		SET 4	
			Weight	Reps	Weight	Reps	Weight	Reps	Weight	Reps

WEDNESDAY	ocus area	Equipment	SET 1		SET 2		SET 3		SET 4	
			Weight	Reps	Weight	Reps	Weight	Reps	Weight	Reps

THURSDAY	ocus area	Equipment	SET 1		SET 2		SET 3		SET 4	
			Weight	Reps	Weight	Reps	Weight	Reps	Weight	Reps

FRIDAY	ocus area	Equipment	SET 1		SET 2		SET 3		SET 4	
			Weight	Reps	Weight	Reps	Weight	Reps	Weight	Reps

SATURDAY	ocus area	Equipment	SET 1		SET 2		SET 3		SET 4	
			Weight	Reps	Weight	Reps	Weight	Reps	Weight	Reps

SUNDAY	ocus area	Equipment	SET 1		SET 2		SET 3		SET 4	
			Weight	Reps	Weight	Reps	Weight	Reps	Weight	Reps

Cardio Training

MONDAY

Exercise	Time	Distance/ resistance	Intensity	Heart rate	Ease	Cal/kJ expended
						Total:

TUESDAY

Exercise	Time	Distance/ resistance	Intensity	Heart rate	Ease	Cal/kJ expended
						Total:

WEDNESDAY

Exercise	Time	Distance/ resistance	Intensity	Heart rate	Ease	Cal/kJ expended
						Total:

THURSDAY

Exercise	Time	Distance/ resistance	Intensity	Heart rate	Ease	Cal/kJ expended
						Total:

FRIDAY

Exercise	Time	Distance/ resistance	Intensity	Heart rate	Ease	Cal/kJ expended
						Total:

SATURDAY

Exercise	Time	Distance/ resistance	Intensity	Heart rate	Ease	Cal/kJ expended
						Total:

SUNDAY

Exercise	Time	Distance/ resistance	Intensity	Heart rate	Ease	Cal/kJ expended
						Total:
						Weekly Total:

Food Diary

MONDAY			Cal/kJ	Fat	Protein	Carbs
Breakfast time: am/pm						
Lunch time: am/pm						
Dinner time: am/pm						
Snacks:						
Coffees/teas:	Fluid intake:	**Totals:**				

TUESDAY			Cal/kJ	Fat	Protein	Carbs
Breakfast time: am/pm						
Lunch time: am/pm						
Dinner time: am/pm						
Snacks:						
Coffees/teas:	Fluid intake:	**Totals:**				

WEDNESDAY			Cal/kJ	Fat	Protein	Carbs
Breakfast time: am/pm						
Lunch time: am/pm						
Dinner time: am/pm						
Snacks:						
Coffees/teas:	Fluid intake:	**Totals:**				

THURSDAY			Cal/kJ	Fat	Protein	Carbs
Breakfast time: am/pm						
Lunch time: am/pm						
Dinner time: am/pm						
Snacks:						
Coffees/teas:	Fluid intake:	**Totals:**				

FRIDAY		Cal/kJ	Fat	Protein	Carbs
Breakfast time: am/pm					
Lunch time: am/pm					
Dinner time: am/pm					
Snacks:					
Coffees/teas:	Fluid intake: **Totals:**				

SATURDAY		Cal/kJ	Fat	Protein	Carbs
Breakfast time: am/pm					
Lunch time: am/pm					
Dinner time: am/pm					
Snacks:					
Coffees/teas:	Fluid intake: **Totals:**				

SUNDAY		Cal/kJ	Fat	Protein	Carbs
Breakfast time: am/pm					
Lunch time: am/pm					
Dinner time: am/pm					
Snacks:					
Coffees/teas:	Fluid intake: **Totals:**				

Units of alcohol this week: Total alcohol Cal/kJ:

Vitamins and supplements

Weekly Totals	Cal/kJ	Fat	Protein	Carbs

Weekly Personal Summary

Energy level (1–5)

Stress level (1–5)

Hours of sleep

Sleep quality (1–5)

Mood (1–5)

Appetite (1–5)

Cal/kJ intake

Planned Cal/kJ	
Actual Cal/kJ	
Difference [+/-]	

Weight at start of week

Weight at end of week

BMI at start of week

BMI at end of week

Injuries or illnesses

Week Beginning

/ /

Strength Training

Planned exercise sessions this week

	Exercise	Completed [Y/N]
Monday		
Tuesday		
Wednesday		
Thursday		
Friday		
Saturday		
Sunday		

MONDAY

Focus area	Equipment	SET 1		SET 2		SET 3		SET 4	
		Weight	Reps	Weight	Reps	Weight	Reps	Weight	Reps

TUESDAY

Focus area	Equipment	SET 1		SET 2		SET 3		SET 4	
		Weight	Reps	Weight	Reps	Weight	Reps	Weight	Reps

WEDNESDAY

Focus area	Equipment	SET 1		SET 2		SET 3		SET 4	
		Weight	Reps	Weight	Reps	Weight	Reps	Weight	Reps

THURSDAY

Focus area	Equipment	SET 1		SET 2		SET 3		SET 4	
		Weight	Reps	Weight	Reps	Weight	Reps	Weight	Reps

FRIDAY

Focus area	Equipment	SET 1		SET 2		SET 3		SET 4	
		Weight	Reps	Weight	Reps	Weight	Reps	Weight	Reps

SATURDAY

Focus area	Equipment	SET 1		SET 2		SET 3		SET 4	
		Weight	Reps	Weight	Reps	Weight	Reps	Weight	Reps

SUNDAY

Focus area	Equipment	SET 1		SET 2		SET 3		SET 4	
		Weight	Reps	Weight	Reps	Weight	Reps	Weight	Reps

Cardio Training

MONDAY	Exercise	Time	Distance/ resistance	Intensity	Heart rate	Ease	Cal/kJ expended
							Total:

TUESDAY	Exercise	Time	Distance/ resistance	Intensity	Heart rate	Ease	Cal/kJ expended
							Total:

WEDNESDAY	Exercise	Time	Distance/ resistance	Intensity	Heart rate	Ease	Cal/kJ expended
							Total:

THURSDAY	Exercise	Time	Distance/ resistance	Intensity	Heart rate	Ease	Cal/kJ expended
							Total:

FRIDAY	Exercise	Time	Distance/ resistance	Intensity	Heart rate	Ease	Cal/kJ expended
							Total:

SATURDAY	Exercise	Time	Distance/ resistance	Intensity	Heart rate	Ease	Cal/kJ expended
							Total:

SUNDAY	Exercise	Time	Distance/ resistance	Intensity	Heart rate	Ease	Cal/kJ expended
							Total:
							Weekly Total:

Food Diary

MONDAY			Cal/kJ	Fat	Protein	Carbs
Breakfast time: am/pm						
Lunch time: am/pm						
Dinner time: am/pm						
Snacks:						
Coffees/teas:	Fluid intake:	**Totals:**				

TUESDAY			Cal/kJ	Fat	Protein	Carbs
Breakfast time: am/pm						
Lunch time: am/pm						
Dinner time: am/pm						
Snacks:						
Coffees/teas:	Fluid intake:	**Totals:**				

WEDNESDAY			Cal/kJ	Fat	Protein	Carbs
Breakfast time: am/pm						
Lunch time: am/pm						
Dinner time: am/pm						
Snacks:						
Coffees/teas:	Fluid intake:	**Totals:**				

THURSDAY			Cal/kJ	Fat	Protein	Carbs
Breakfast time: am/pm						
Lunch time: am/pm						
Dinner time: am/pm						
Snacks:						
Coffees/teas:	Fluid intake:	**Totals:**				

FRIDAY		Cal/kJ	Fat	Protein	Carbs
Breakfast time: am/pm					
Lunch time: am/pm					
Dinner time: am/pm					
Snacks:					
Coffees/teas:	Fluid intake: Totals:				

SATURDAY		Cal/kJ	Fat	Protein	Carbs
Breakfast time: am/pm					
Lunch time: am/pm					
Dinner time: am/pm					
Snacks:					
Coffees/teas:	Fluid intake: Totals:				

SUNDAY		Cal/kJ	Fat	Protein	Carbs
Breakfast time: am/pm					
Lunch time: am/pm					
Dinner time: am/pm					
Snacks:					
Coffees/teas:	Fluid intake: Totals:				

Units of alcohol this week: Total alcohol Cal/kJ:

Vitamins and supplements

Weekly Totals	Cal/kJ	Fat	Protein	Carbs

Weekly Personal Summary

Energy level (1–5)

Stress level (1–5)

Hours of sleep

Sleep quality (1–5)

Mood (1–5)

Appetite (1–5)

Cal/kJ intake

Planned Cal/kJ	
Actual Cal/kJ	
Difference [+/-]	

Weight at start of week

Weight at end of week

BMI at start of week

BMI at end of week

Injuries or illnesses

Week Beginning

/ /

Strength Training

Planned exercise sessions this week

	Exercise	Completed [Y/N]
Monday		
Tuesday		
Wednesday		
Thursday		
Friday		
Saturday		
Sunday		

	ocus area	Equipment	SET 1		SET 2		SET 3		SET 4	
			Weight	Reps	Weight	Reps	Weight	Reps	Weight	Reps
MONDAY										

	ocus area	Equipment	SET 1		SET 2		SET 3		SET 4	
			Weight	Reps	Weight	Reps	Weight	Reps	Weight	Reps
TUESDAY										

	ocus area	Equipment	SET 1		SET 2		SET 3		SET 4	
			Weight	Reps	Weight	Reps	Weight	Reps	Weight	Reps
WEDNESDAY										

	ocus area	Equipment	SET 1		SET 2		SET 3		SET 4	
			Weight	Reps	Weight	Reps	Weight	Reps	Weight	Reps
THURSDAY										

	ocus area	Equipment	SET 1		SET 2		SET 3		SET 4	
			Weight	Reps	Weight	Reps	Weight	Reps	Weight	Reps
FRIDAY										

	ocus area	Equipment	SET 1		SET 2		SET 3		SET 4	
			Weight	Reps	Weight	Reps	Weight	Reps	Weight	Reps
SATURDAY										

	ocus area	Equipment	SET 1		SET 2		SET 3		SET 4	
			Weight	Reps	Weight	Reps	Weight	Reps	Weight	Reps
SUNDAY										

Cardio Training

MONDAY

Exercise	Time	Distance/ resistance	Intensity	Heart rate	Ease	Cal/kJ expended
						Total:

TUESDAY

Exercise	Time	Distance/ resistance	Intensity	Heart rate	Ease	Cal/kJ expended
						Total:

WEDNESDAY

Exercise	Time	Distance/ resistance	Intensity	Heart rate	Ease	Cal/kJ expended
						Total:

THURSDAY

Exercise	Time	Distance/ resistance	Intensity	Heart rate	Ease	Cal/kJ expended
						Total:

FRIDAY

Exercise	Time	Distance/ resistance	Intensity	Heart rate	Ease	Cal/kJ expended
						Total:

SATURDAY

Exercise	Time	Distance/ resistance	Intensity	Heart rate	Ease	Cal/kJ expended
						Total:

SUNDAY

Exercise	Time	Distance/ resistance	Intensity	Heart rate	Ease	Cal/kJ expended
						Total:
						Weekly Total:

Food Diary

MONDAY			Cal/kJ	Fat	Protein	Carbs
Breakfast time: am/pm						
Lunch time: am/pm						
Dinner time: am/pm						
Snacks:						
Coffees/teas:	Fluid intake:	**Totals:**				

TUESDAY			Cal/kJ	Fat	Protein	Carbs
Breakfast time: am/pm						
Lunch time: am/pm						
Dinner time: am/pm						
Snacks:						
Coffees/teas:	Fluid intake:	**Totals:**				

WEDNESDAY			Cal/kJ	Fat	Protein	Carbs
Breakfast time: am/pm						
Lunch time: am/pm						
Dinner time: am/pm						
Snacks:						
Coffees/teas:	Fluid intake:	**Totals:**				

THURSDAY			Cal/kJ	Fat	Protein	Carbs
Breakfast time: am/pm						
Lunch time: am/pm						
Dinner time: am/pm						
Snacks:						
Coffees/teas:	Fluid intake:	**Totals:**				

FRIDAY		Cal/kJ	Fat	Protein	Carbs
Breakfast time: am/pm					
Lunch time: am/pm					
Dinner time: am/pm					
Snacks:					
Coffees/teas:	Fluid intake: **Totals:**				

SATURDAY		Cal/kJ	Fat	Protein	Carbs
Breakfast time: am/pm					
Lunch time: am/pm					
Dinner time: am/pm					
Snacks:					
Coffees/teas:	Fluid intake: **Totals:**				

SUNDAY		Cal/kJ	Fat	Protein	Carbs
Breakfast time: am/pm					
Lunch time: am/pm					
Dinner time: am/pm					
Snacks:					
Coffees/teas:	Fluid intake: **Totals:**				

Units of alcohol this week: Total alcohol Cal/kJ:

Vitamins and supplements

Weekly Totals	Cal/kJ	Fat	Protein	Carbs

Weekly Personal Summary

Energy level (1–5)

Stress level (1–5)

Hours of sleep

Sleep quality (1–5)

Mood (1–5)

Appetite (1–5)

Cal/kJ intake

Planned Cal/kJ	
Actual Cal/kJ	

Difference [+/-]

Weight at start of week

Weight at end of week

BMI at start of week

BMI at end of week

Injuries or illnesses

Week Beginning

/ /

Planned exercise sessions this week

	Exercise	Completed [Y/N]
Monday		
Tuesday		
Wednesday		
Thursday		
Friday		
Saturday		
Sunday		

Strength Training

MONDAY	ocus area	Equipment	SET 1		SET 2		SET 3		SET 4	
			Weight	Reps	Weight	Reps	Weight	Reps	Weight	Reps

TUESDAY	ocus area	Equipment	SET 1		SET 2		SET 3		SET 4	
			Weight	Reps	Weight	Reps	Weight	Reps	Weight	Reps

WEDNESDAY	ocus area	Equipment	SET 1		SET 2		SET 3		SET 4	
			Weight	Reps	Weight	Reps	Weight	Reps	Weight	Reps

THURSDAY	ocus area	Equipment	SET 1		SET 2		SET 3		SET 4	
			Weight	Reps	Weight	Reps	Weight	Reps	Weight	Reps

FRIDAY	ocus area	Equipment	SET 1		SET 2		SET 3		SET 4	
			Weight	Reps	Weight	Reps	Weight	Reps	Weight	Reps

SATURDAY	ocus area	Equipment	SET 1		SET 2		SET 3		SET 4	
			Weight	Reps	Weight	Reps	Weight	Reps	Weight	Reps

SUNDAY	ocus area	Equipment	SET 1		SET 2		SET 3		SET 4	
			Weight	Reps	Weight	Reps	Weight	Reps	Weight	Reps

Cardio Training

MONDAY

Exercise	Time	Distance/ resistance	Intensity	Heart rate	Ease	Cal/kJ expended
						Total:

TUESDAY

Exercise	Time	Distance/ resistance	Intensity	Heart rate	Ease	Cal/kJ expended
						Total:

WEDNESDAY

Exercise	Time	Distance/ resistance	Intensity	Heart rate	Ease	Cal/kJ expended
						Total:

THURSDAY

Exercise	Time	Distance/ resistance	Intensity	Heart rate	Ease	Cal/kJ expended
						Total:

FRIDAY

Exercise	Time	Distance/ resistance	Intensity	Heart rate	Ease	Cal/kJ expended
						Total:

SATURDAY

Exercise	Time	Distance/ resistance	Intensity	Heart rate	Ease	Cal/kJ expended
						Total:

SUNDAY

Exercise	Time	Distance/ resistance	Intensity	Heart rate	Ease	Cal/kJ expended
						Total:
					Weekly Total:	

Food Diary

MONDAY	Cal/kJ	Fat	Protein	Carbs
Breakfast time: am/pm				
Lunch time: am/pm				
Dinner time: am/pm				
Snacks:				
Coffees/teas: Fluid intake: **Totals:**				

TUESDAY	Cal/kJ	Fat	Protein	Carbs
Breakfast time: am/pm				
Lunch time: am/pm				
Dinner time: am/pm				
Snacks:				
Coffees/teas: Fluid intake: **Totals:**				

WEDNESDAY	Cal/kJ	Fat	Protein	Carbs
Breakfast time: am/pm				
Lunch time: am/pm				
Dinner time: am/pm				
Snacks:				
Coffees/teas: Fluid intake: **Totals:**				

THURSDAY	Cal/kJ	Fat	Protein	Carbs
Breakfast time: am/pm				
Lunch time: am/pm				
Dinner time: am/pm				
Snacks:				
Coffees/teas: Fluid intake: **Totals:**				

FRIDAY		Cal/kJ	Fat	Protein	Carbs
Breakfast time: am/pm					
Lunch time: am/pm					
Dinner time: am/pm					
Snacks:					
Coffees/teas:	Fluid intake: **Totals:**				

SATURDAY		Cal/kJ	Fat	Protein	Carbs
Breakfast time: am/pm					
Lunch time: am/pm					
Dinner time: am/pm					
Snacks:					
Coffees/teas:	Fluid intake: **Totals:**				

SUNDAY		Cal/kJ	Fat	Protein	Carbs
Breakfast time: am/pm					
Lunch time: am/pm					
Dinner time: am/pm					
Snacks:					
Coffees/teas:	Fluid intake: **Totals:**				

Units of alcohol this week: ____ Total alcohol Cal/kJ: ____

Vitamins and supplements

Weekly Totals	Cal/kJ	Fat	Protein	Carbs

Weekly Personal Summary

Energy level (1–5) ____ Stress level (1–5) ____

Hours of sleep ____ Sleep quality (1–5) ____

Mood (1–5) ____ Appetite (1–5) ____

Cal/kJ intake

Planned Cal/kJ	
Actual Cal/kJ	
Difference [+/-]	

Weight at start of week ____

Weight at end of week ____

BMI at start of week ____

BMI at end of week ____

Injuries or illnesses ____

Week Beginning

/ /

Planned exercise sessions this week

	Exercise	Completed [Y/N]
Monday		
Tuesday		
Wednesday		
Thursday		
Friday		
Saturday		
Sunday		

Strength Training

MONDAY

Focus area	Equipment	SET 1		SET 2		SET 3		SET 4	
		Weight	Reps	Weight	Reps	Weight	Reps	Weight	Reps

TUESDAY

Focus area	Equipment	SET 1		SET 2		SET 3		SET 4	
		Weight	Reps	Weight	Reps	Weight	Reps	Weight	Reps

WEDNESDAY

Focus area	Equipment	SET 1		SET 2		SET 3		SET 4	
		Weight	Reps	Weight	Reps	Weight	Reps	Weight	Reps

THURSDAY

Focus area	Equipment	SET 1		SET 2		SET 3		SET 4	
		Weight	Reps	Weight	Reps	Weight	Reps	Weight	Reps

FRIDAY

Focus area	Equipment	SET 1		SET 2		SET 3		SET 4	
		Weight	Reps	Weight	Reps	Weight	Reps	Weight	Reps

SATURDAY

Focus area	Equipment	SET 1		SET 2		SET 3		SET 4	
		Weight	Reps	Weight	Reps	Weight	Reps	Weight	Reps

SUNDAY

Focus area	Equipment	SET 1		SET 2		SET 3		SET 4	
		Weight	Reps	Weight	Reps	Weight	Reps	Weight	Reps

Cardio Training

MONDAY	Exercise	Time	Distance/ resistance	Intensity	Heart rate	Ease	Cal/kJ expended
							Total:

TUESDAY	Exercise	Time	Distance/ resistance	Intensity	Heart rate	Ease	Cal/kJ expended
							Total:

WEDNESDAY	Exercise	Time	Distance/ resistance	Intensity	Heart rate	Ease	Cal/kJ expended
							Total:

THURSDAY	Exercise	Time	Distance/ resistance	Intensity	Heart rate	Ease	Cal/kJ expended
							Total:

FRIDAY	Exercise	Time	Distance/ resistance	Intensity	Heart rate	Ease	Cal/kJ expended
							Total:

SATURDAY	Exercise	Time	Distance/ resistance	Intensity	Heart rate	Ease	Cal/kJ expended
							Total:

SUNDAY	Exercise	Time	Distance/ resistance	Intensity	Heart rate	Ease	Cal/kJ expended
							Total:
							Weekly Total:

Food Diary

MONDAY		Cal/kJ	Fat	Protein	Carbs
Breakfast time: am/pm					
Lunch time: am/pm					
Dinner time: am/pm					
Snacks:					
Coffees/teas:	Fluid intake:	**Totals:**			

TUESDAY		Cal/kJ	Fat	Protein	Carbs
Breakfast time: am/pm					
Lunch time: am/pm					
Dinner time: am/pm					
Snacks:					
Coffees/teas:	Fluid intake:	**Totals:**			

WEDNESDAY		Cal/kJ	Fat	Protein	Carbs
Breakfast time: am/pm					
Lunch time: am/pm					
Dinner time: am/pm					
Snacks:					
Coffees/teas:	Fluid intake:	**Totals:**			

THURSDAY		Cal/kJ	Fat	Protein	Carbs
Breakfast time: am/pm					
Lunch time: am/pm					
Dinner time: am/pm					
Snacks:					
Coffees/teas:	Fluid intake:	**Totals:**			

FRIDAY		Cal/kJ	Fat	Protein	Carbs
Breakfast time: am/pm					
Lunch time: am/pm					
Dinner time: am/pm					
Snacks:					
Coffees/teas:	Fluid intake: **Totals:**				

SATURDAY		Cal/kJ	Fat	Protein	Carbs
Breakfast time: am/pm					
Lunch time: am/pm					
Dinner time: am/pm					
Snacks:					
Coffees/teas:	Fluid intake: **Totals:**				

SUNDAY		Cal/kJ	Fat	Protein	Carbs
Breakfast time: am/pm					
Lunch time: am/pm					
Dinner time: am/pm					
Snacks:					
Coffees/teas:	Fluid intake: **Totals:**				

Units of alcohol this week: Total alcohol Cal/kJ:

Vitamins and supplements

Weekly Totals	Cal/kJ	Fat	Protein	Carbs

Weekly Personal Summary

Energy level (1–5)

Stress level (1–5)

Hours of sleep

Sleep quality (1–5)

Mood (1–5)

Appetite (1–5)

Cal/kJ intake

Planned Cal/kJ	
Actual Cal/kJ	

Difference [+/–]

Weight at start of week

Weight at end of week

BMI at start of week

BMI at end of week

Injuries or illnesses

Week Beginning

/ /

Planned exercise sessions this week

	Exercise	Completed [Y/N]
Monday		
Tuesday		
Wednesday		
Thursday		
Friday		
Saturday		
Sunday		

Strength Training

MONDAY	Focus area	Equipment	SET 1		SET 2		SET 3		SET 4	
			Weight	Reps	Weight	Reps	Weight	Reps	Weight	Reps

TUESDAY	Focus area	Equipment	SET 1		SET 2		SET 3		SET 4	
			Weight	Reps	Weight	Reps	Weight	Reps	Weight	Reps

WEDNESDAY	Focus area	Equipment	SET 1		SET 2		SET 3		SET 4	
			Weight	Reps	Weight	Reps	Weight	Reps	Weight	Reps

THURSDAY	Focus area	Equipment	SET 1		SET 2		SET 3		SET 4	
			Weight	Reps	Weight	Reps	Weight	Reps	Weight	Reps

FRIDAY	Focus area	Equipment	SET 1		SET 2		SET 3		SET 4	
			Weight	Reps	Weight	Reps	Weight	Reps	Weight	Reps

SATURDAY	Focus area	Equipment	SET 1		SET 2		SET 3		SET 4	
			Weight	Reps	Weight	Reps	Weight	Reps	Weight	Reps

SUNDAY	Focus area	Equipment	SET 1		SET 2		SET 3		SET 4	
			Weight	Reps	Weight	Reps	Weight	Reps	Weight	Reps

Cardio Training

MONDAY	Exercise	Time	Distance/ resistance	Intensity	Heart rate	Ease	Cal/kJ expended
							Total:

TUESDAY	Exercise	Time	Distance/ resistance	Intensity	Heart rate	Ease	Cal/kJ expended
							Total:

WEDNESDAY	Exercise	Time	Distance/ resistance	Intensity	Heart rate	Ease	Cal/kJ expended
							Total:

THURSDAY	Exercise	Time	Distance/ resistance	Intensity	Heart rate	Ease	Cal/kJ expended
							Total:

FRIDAY	Exercise	Time	Distance/ resistance	Intensity	Heart rate	Ease	Cal/kJ expended
							Total:

SATURDAY	Exercise	Time	Distance/ resistance	Intensity	Heart rate	Ease	Cal/kJ expended
							Total:

SUNDAY	Exercise	Time	Distance/ resistance	Intensity	Heart rate	Ease	Cal/kJ expended
							Total:
							Weekly Total:

Food Diary

MONDAY			Cal/kJ	Fat	Protein	Carbs
Breakfast time: am/pm						
Lunch time: am/pm						
Dinner time: am/pm						
Snacks:						
Coffees/teas:	Fluid intake:	**Totals:**				

TUESDAY			Cal/kJ	Fat	Protein	Carbs
Breakfast time: am/pm						
Lunch time: am/pm						
Dinner time: am/pm						
Snacks:						
Coffees/teas:	Fluid intake:	**Totals:**				

WEDNESDAY			Cal/kJ	Fat	Protein	Carbs
Breakfast time: am/pm						
Lunch time: am/pm						
Dinner time: am/pm						
Snacks:						
Coffees/teas:	Fluid intake:	**Totals:**				

THURSDAY			Cal/kJ	Fat	Protein	Carbs
Breakfast time: am/pm						
Lunch time: am/pm						
Dinner time: am/pm						
Snacks:						
Coffees/teas:	Fluid intake:	**Totals:**				

FRIDAY		Cal/kJ	Fat	Protein	Carbs
Breakfast time: am/pm					
Lunch time: am/pm					
Dinner time: am/pm					
Snacks:					
Coffees/teas:	Fluid intake: **Totals:**				

SATURDAY		Cal/kJ	Fat	Protein	Carbs
Breakfast time: am/pm					
Lunch time: am/pm					
Dinner time: am/pm					
Snacks:					
Coffees/teas:	Fluid intake: **Totals:**				

SUNDAY		Cal/kJ	Fat	Protein	Carbs
Breakfast time: am/pm					
Lunch time: am/pm					
Dinner time: am/pm					
Snacks:					
Coffees/teas:	Fluid intake: **Totals:**				

Units of alcohol this week: ______ Total alcohol Cal/kJ: ______

Vitamins and supplements

Weekly Totals	Cal/kJ	Fat	Protein	Carbs

Weekly Personal Summary

Energy level (1–5) ______ Stress level (1–5) ______

Hours of sleep ______ Sleep quality (1–5) ______

Mood (1–5) ______ Appetite (1–5) ______

Cal/kJ intake

Planned Cal/kJ	
Actual Cal/kJ	

Difference [+/-] ______

Weight at start of week ______

Weight at end of week ______

BMI at start of week ______

BMI at end of week ______

Injuries or illnesses ______

Week Beginning

/ /

Strength Training

Planned exercise sessions this week

	Exercise	Completed [Y/N]
Monday		
Tuesday		
Wednesday		
Thursday		
Friday		
Saturday		
Sunday		

MONDAY	Focus area	Equipment	SET 1		SET 2		SET 3		SET 4	
			Weight	Reps	Weight	Reps	Weight	Reps	Weight	Reps

TUESDAY	Focus area	Equipment	SET 1		SET 2		SET 3		SET 4	
			Weight	Reps	Weight	Reps	Weight	Reps	Weight	Reps

WEDNESDAY	Focus area	Equipment	SET 1		SET 2		SET 3		SET 4	
			Weight	Reps	Weight	Reps	Weight	Reps	Weight	Reps

THURSDAY	Focus area	Equipment	SET 1		SET 2		SET 3		SET 4	
			Weight	Reps	Weight	Reps	Weight	Reps	Weight	Reps

FRIDAY	Focus area	Equipment	SET 1		SET 2		SET 3		SET 4	
			Weight	Reps	Weight	Reps	Weight	Reps	Weight	Reps

SATURDAY	Focus area	Equipment	SET 1		SET 2		SET 3		SET 4	
			Weight	Reps	Weight	Reps	Weight	Reps	Weight	Reps

SUNDAY	Focus area	Equipment	SET 1		SET 2		SET 3		SET 4	
			Weight	Reps	Weight	Reps	Weight	Reps	Weight	Reps

Cardio Training

MONDAY

Exercise	Time	Distance/ resistance	Intensity	Heart rate	Ease	Cal/kJ expended
						Total:

TUESDAY

Exercise	Time	Distance/ resistance	Intensity	Heart rate	Ease	Cal/kJ expended
						Total:

WEDNESDAY

Exercise	Time	Distance/ resistance	Intensity	Heart rate	Ease	Cal/kJ expended
						Total:

THURSDAY

Exercise	Time	Distance/ resistance	Intensity	Heart rate	Ease	Cal/kJ expended
						Total:

FRIDAY

Exercise	Time	Distance/ resistance	Intensity	Heart rate	Ease	Cal/kJ expended
						Total:

SATURDAY

Exercise	Time	Distance/ resistance	Intensity	Heart rate	Ease	Cal/kJ expended
						Total:

SUNDAY

Exercise	Time	Distance/ resistance	Intensity	Heart rate	Ease	Cal/kJ expended
						Total:

Weekly Total:

Food Diary

MONDAY			Cal/kJ	Fat	Protein	Carbs
Breakfast time: am/pm						
Lunch time: am/pm						
Dinner time: am/pm						
Snacks:						
Coffees/teas:	Fluid intake:	**Totals:**				

TUESDAY			Cal/kJ	Fat	Protein	Carbs
Breakfast time: am/pm						
Lunch time: am/pm						
Dinner time: am/pm						
Snacks:						
Coffees/teas:	Fluid intake:	**Totals:**				

WEDNESDAY			Cal/kJ	Fat	Protein	Carbs
Breakfast time: am/pm						
Lunch time: am/pm						
Dinner time: am/pm						
Snacks:						
Coffees/teas:	Fluid intake:	**Totals:**				

THURSDAY			Cal/kJ	Fat	Protein	Carbs
Breakfast time: am/pm						
Lunch time: am/pm						
Dinner time: am/pm						
Snacks:						
Coffees/teas:	Fluid intake:	**Totals:**				

FRIDAY			Cal/kJ	Fat	Protein	Carbs
Breakfast time: am/pm						
Lunch time: am/pm						
Dinner time: am/pm						
Snacks:						
Coffees/teas:	Fluid intake:	**Totals:**				

SATURDAY			Cal/kJ	Fat	Protein	Carbs
Breakfast time: am/pm						
Lunch time: am/pm						
Dinner time: am/pm						
Snacks:						
Coffees/teas:	Fluid intake:	**Totals:**				

SUNDAY			Cal/kJ	Fat	Protein	Carbs
Breakfast time: am/pm						
Lunch time: am/pm						
Dinner time: am/pm						
Snacks:						
Coffees/teas:	Fluid intake:	**Totals:**				

Units of alcohol this week: Total alcohol Cal/kJ:

Vitamins and supplements

	Cal/kJ	Fat	Protein	Carbs
Weekly Totals				

Weekly Personal Summary

Energy level (1–5)

Stress level (1–5)

Hours of sleep

Sleep quality (1–5)

Mood (1–5)

Appetite (1–5)

Cal/kJ intake

Planned Cal/kJ	
Actual Cal/kJ	

Difference [+/-]

Weight at start of week

Weight at end of week

BMI at start of week

BMI at end of week

Injuries or illnesses

Week Beginning

/ /

Strength Training

Planned exercise sessions this week

	Exercise	Completed [Y/N]
Monday		
Tuesday		
Wednesday		
Thursday		
Friday		
Saturday		
Sunday		

MONDAY

Focus area	Equipment	SET 1		SET 2		SET 3		SET 4	
		Weight	Reps	Weight	Reps	Weight	Reps	Weight	Reps

TUESDAY

Focus area	Equipment	SET 1		SET 2		SET 3		SET 4	
		Weight	Reps	Weight	Reps	Weight	Reps	Weight	Reps

WEDNESDAY

Focus area	Equipment	SET 1		SET 2		SET 3		SET 4	
		Weight	Reps	Weight	Reps	Weight	Reps	Weight	Reps

THURSDAY

Focus area	Equipment	SET 1		SET 2		SET 3		SET 4	
		Weight	Reps	Weight	Reps	Weight	Reps	Weight	Reps

FRIDAY

Focus area	Equipment	SET 1		SET 2		SET 3		SET 4	
		Weight	Reps	Weight	Reps	Weight	Reps	Weight	Reps

SATURDAY

Focus area	Equipment	SET 1		SET 2		SET 3		SET 4	
		Weight	Reps	Weight	Reps	Weight	Reps	Weight	Reps

SUNDAY

Focus area	Equipment	SET 1		SET 2		SET 3		SET 4	
		Weight	Reps	Weight	Reps	Weight	Reps	Weight	Reps

Cardio Training

MONDAY

Exercise	Time	Distance/ resistance	Intensity	Heart rate	Ease	Cal/kJ expended
						Total:

TUESDAY

Exercise	Time	Distance/ resistance	Intensity	Heart rate	Ease	Cal/kJ expended
						Total:

WEDNESDAY

Exercise	Time	Distance/ resistance	Intensity	Heart rate	Ease	Cal/kJ expended
						Total:

THURSDAY

Exercise	Time	Distance/ resistance	Intensity	Heart rate	Ease	Cal/kJ expended
						Total:

FRIDAY

Exercise	Time	Distance/ resistance	Intensity	Heart rate	Ease	Cal/kJ expended
						Total:

SATURDAY

Exercise	Time	Distance/ resistance	Intensity	Heart rate	Ease	Cal/kJ expended
						Total:

SUNDAY

Exercise	Time	Distance/ resistance	Intensity	Heart rate	Ease	Cal/kJ expended
						Total:
						Weekly Total:

Food Diary

MONDAY		Cal/kJ	Fat	Protein	Carbs
Breakfast time: am/pm					
Lunch time: am/pm					
Dinner time: am/pm					
Snacks:					
Coffees/teas:	Fluid intake: **Totals:**				

TUESDAY		Cal/kJ	Fat	Protein	Carbs
Breakfast time: am/pm					
Lunch time: am/pm					
Dinner time: am/pm					
Snacks:					
Coffees/teas:	Fluid intake: **Totals:**				

WEDNESDAY		Cal/kJ	Fat	Protein	Carbs
Breakfast time: am/pm					
Lunch time: am/pm					
Dinner time: am/pm					
Snacks:					
Coffees/teas:	Fluid intake: **Totals:**				

THURSDAY		Cal/kJ	Fat	Protein	Carbs
Breakfast time: am/pm					
Lunch time: am/pm					
Dinner time: am/pm					
Snacks:					
Coffees/teas:	Fluid intake: **Totals:**				

FRIDAY		Cal/kJ	Fat	Protein	Carbs
Breakfast time: am/pm					
Lunch time: am/pm					
Dinner time: am/pm					
Snacks:					
Coffees/teas:	Fluid intake: **Totals:**				

SATURDAY		Cal/kJ	Fat	Protein	Carbs
Breakfast time: am/pm					
Lunch time: am/pm					
Dinner time: am/pm					
Snacks:					
Coffees/teas:	Fluid intake: **Totals:**				

SUNDAY		Cal/kJ	Fat	Protein	Carbs
Breakfast time: am/pm					
Lunch time: am/pm					
Dinner time: am/pm					
Snacks:					
Coffees/teas:	Fluid intake: **Totals:**				

Units of alcohol this week: Total alcohol Cal/kJ:

Vitamins and supplements

Weekly Totals	Cal/kJ	Fat	Protein	Carbs

Weekly Personal Summary

Energy level (1–5)

Stress level (1–5)

Hours of sleep

Sleep quality (1–5)

Mood (1–5)

Appetite (1–5)

Cal/kJ intake

Planned Cal/kJ	
Actual Cal/kJ	
Difference [+/-]	

Weight at start of week

Weight at end of week

BMI at start of week

BMI at end of week

Injuries or illnesses

Week Beginning

/ /

Strength Training

Planned exercise sessions this week

	Exercise	Completed [Y/N]
Monday		
Tuesday		
Wednesday		
Thursday		
Friday		
Saturday		
Sunday		

MONDAY	ocus area	Equipment	SET 1		SET 2		SET 3		SET 4	
			Weight	Reps	Weight	Reps	Weight	Reps	Weight	Reps

TUESDAY	ocus area	Equipment	SET 1		SET 2		SET 3		SET 4	
			Weight	Reps	Weight	Reps	Weight	Reps	Weight	Reps

WEDNESDAY	ocus area	Equipment	SET 1		SET 2		SET 3		SET 4	
			Weight	Reps	Weight	Reps	Weight	Reps	Weight	Reps

THURSDAY	ocus area	Equipment	SET 1		SET 2		SET 3		SET 4	
			Weight	Reps	Weight	Reps	Weight	Reps	Weight	Reps

FRIDAY	ocus area	Equipment	SET 1		SET 2		SET 3		SET 4	
			Weight	Reps	Weight	Reps	Weight	Reps	Weight	Reps

SATURDAY	ocus area	Equipment	SET 1		SET 2		SET 3		SET 4	
			Weight	Reps	Weight	Reps	Weight	Reps	Weight	Reps

SUNDAY	ocus area	Equipment	SET 1		SET 2		SET 3		SET 4	
			Weight	Reps	Weight	Reps	Weight	Reps	Weight	Reps

Cardio Training

MONDAY

Exercise	Time	Distance/ resistance	Intensity	Heart rate	Ease	Cal/kJ expended
						Total:

TUESDAY

Exercise	Time	Distance/ resistance	Intensity	Heart rate	Ease	Cal/kJ expended
						Total:

WEDNESDAY

Exercise	Time	Distance/ resistance	Intensity	Heart rate	Ease	Cal/kJ expended
						Total:

THURSDAY

Exercise	Time	Distance/ resistance	Intensity	Heart rate	Ease	Cal/kJ expended
						Total:

FRIDAY

Exercise	Time	Distance/ resistance	Intensity	Heart rate	Ease	Cal/kJ expended
						Total:

SATURDAY

Exercise	Time	Distance/ resistance	Intensity	Heart rate	Ease	Cal/kJ expended
						Total:

SUNDAY

Exercise	Time	Distance/ resistance	Intensity	Heart rate	Ease	Cal/kJ expended
						Total:
						Weekly Total:

Food Diary

MONDAY		Cal/kJ	Fat	Protein	Carbs
Breakfast time: am/pm					
Lunch time: am/pm					
Dinner time: am/pm					
Snacks:					
Coffees/teas:	Fluid intake: **Totals:**				

TUESDAY		Cal/kJ	Fat	Protein	Carbs
Breakfast time: am/pm					
Lunch time: am/pm					
Dinner time: am/pm					
Snacks:					
Coffees/teas:	Fluid intake: **Totals:**				

WEDNESDAY		Cal/kJ	Fat	Protein	Carbs
Breakfast time: am/pm					
Lunch time: am/pm					
Dinner time: am/pm					
Snacks:					
Coffees/teas:	Fluid intake: **Totals:**				

THURSDAY		Cal/kJ	Fat	Protein	Carbs
Breakfast time: am/pm					
Lunch time: am/pm					
Dinner time: am/pm					
Snacks:					
Coffees/teas:	Fluid intake: **Totals:**				

FRIDAY			Cal/kJ	Fat	Protein	Carbs
Breakfast time: am/pm						
Lunch time: am/pm						
Dinner time: am/pm						
Snacks:						
Coffees/teas:	Fluid intake:	**Totals:**				

SATURDAY			Cal/kJ	Fat	Protein	Carbs
Breakfast time: am/pm						
Lunch time: am/pm						
Dinner time: am/pm						
Snacks:						
Coffees/teas:	Fluid intake:	**Totals:**				

SUNDAY			Cal/kJ	Fat	Protein	Carbs
Breakfast time: am/pm						
Lunch time: am/pm						
Dinner time: am/pm						
Snacks:						
Coffees/teas:	Fluid intake:	**Totals:**				

Units of alcohol this week: Total alcohol Cal/kJ:

Vitamins and supplements

Weekly Totals	Cal/kJ	Fat	Protein	Carbs

Weekly Personal Summary

Energy level (1–5) Stress level (1–5)

Hours of sleep Sleep quality (1–5)

Mood (1–5) Appetite (1–5)

Cal/kJ intake

Planned Cal/kJ	
Actual Cal/kJ	

Difference [+/-]

Weight at start of week

Weight at end of week

BMI at start of week

BMI at end of week

Injuries or illnesses

Week Beginning

/ /

Planned exercise sessions this week

	Exercise	Completed [Y/N]
Monday		
Tuesday		
Wednesday		
Thursday		
Friday		
Saturday		
Sunday		

Strength Training

MONDAY	Focus area	Equipment	SET 1		SET 2		SET 3		SET 4	
			Weight	Reps	Weight	Reps	Weight	Reps	Weight	Reps

TUESDAY	Focus area	Equipment	SET 1		SET 2		SET 3		SET 4	
			Weight	Reps	Weight	Reps	Weight	Reps	Weight	Reps

WEDNESDAY	Focus area	Equipment	SET 1		SET 2		SET 3		SET 4	
			Weight	Reps	Weight	Reps	Weight	Reps	Weight	Reps

THURSDAY	Focus area	Equipment	SET 1		SET 2		SET 3		SET 4	
			Weight	Reps	Weight	Reps	Weight	Reps	Weight	Reps

FRIDAY	Focus area	Equipment	SET 1		SET 2		SET 3		SET 4	
			Weight	Reps	Weight	Reps	Weight	Reps	Weight	Reps

SATURDAY	Focus area	Equipment	SET 1		SET 2		SET 3		SET 4	
			Weight	Reps	Weight	Reps	Weight	Reps	Weight	Reps

SUNDAY	Focus area	Equipment	SET 1		SET 2		SET 3		SET 4	
			Weight	Reps	Weight	Reps	Weight	Reps	Weight	Reps

Cardio Training

MONDAY

Exercise	Time	Distance/ resistance	Intensity	Heart rate	Ease	Cal/kJ expended
						Total:

TUESDAY

Exercise	Time	Distance/ resistance	Intensity	Heart rate	Ease	Cal/kJ expended
						Total:

WEDNESDAY

Exercise	Time	Distance/ resistance	Intensity	Heart rate	Ease	Cal/kJ expended
						Total:

THURSDAY

Exercise	Time	Distance/ resistance	Intensity	Heart rate	Ease	Cal/kJ expended
						Total:

FRIDAY

Exercise	Time	Distance/ resistance	Intensity	Heart rate	Ease	Cal/kJ expended
						Total:

SATURDAY

Exercise	Time	Distance/ resistance	Intensity	Heart rate	Ease	Cal/kJ expended
						Total:

SUNDAY

Exercise	Time	Distance/ resistance	Intensity	Heart rate	Ease	Cal/kJ expended
						Total:

Weekly Total:

Food Diary

MONDAY		Cal/kJ	Fat	Protein	Carbs
Breakfast time: am/pm					
Lunch time: am/pm					
Dinner time: am/pm					
Snacks:					
Coffees/teas:	Fluid intake: **Totals:**				

TUESDAY		Cal/kJ	Fat	Protein	Carbs
Breakfast time: am/pm					
Lunch time: am/pm					
Dinner time: am/pm					
Snacks:					
Coffees/teas:	Fluid intake: **Totals:**				

WEDNESDAY		Cal/kJ	Fat	Protein	Carbs
Breakfast time: am/pm					
Lunch time: am/pm					
Dinner time: am/pm					
Snacks:					
Coffees/teas:	Fluid intake: **Totals:**				

THURSDAY		Cal/kJ	Fat	Protein	Carbs
Breakfast time: am/pm					
Lunch time: am/pm					
Dinner time: am/pm					
Snacks:					
Coffees/teas:	Fluid intake: **Totals:**				

FRIDAY		Cal/kJ	Fat	Protein	Carbs
Breakfast time: am/pm					
Lunch time: am/pm					
Dinner time: am/pm					
Snacks:					
Coffees/teas:	Fluid intake: **Totals:**				

SATURDAY		Cal/kJ	Fat	Protein	Carbs
Breakfast time: am/pm					
Lunch time: am/pm					
Dinner time: am/pm					
Snacks:					
Coffees/teas:	Fluid intake: **Totals:**				

SUNDAY		Cal/kJ	Fat	Protein	Carbs
Breakfast time: am/pm					
Lunch time: am/pm					
Dinner time: am/pm					
Snacks:					
Coffees/teas:	Fluid intake: **Totals:**				

Units of alcohol this week: Total alcohol Cal/kJ:

Vitamins and supplements

Weekly Totals	Cal/kJ	Fat	Protein	Carbs

Weekly Personal Summary

Energy level (1–5)

Stress level (1–5)

Hours of sleep

Sleep quality (1–5)

Mood (1–5)

Appetite (1–5)

Cal/kJ intake

Planned Cal/kJ	
Actual Cal/kJ	

Difference [+/-]

Weight at start of week

Weight at end of week

BMI at start of week

BMI at end of week

Injuries or illnesses

Week Beginning

/ /

Planned exercise sessions this week

	Exercise	Completed [Y/N]
Monday		
Tuesday		
Wednesday		
Thursday		
Friday		
Saturday		
Sunday		

Strength Training

MONDAY	ocus area	Equipment	SET 1		SET 2		SET 3		SET 4	
			Weight	Reps	Weight	Reps	Weight	Reps	Weight	Reps

TUESDAY	ocus area	Equipment	SET 1		SET 2		SET 3		SET 4	
			Weight	Reps	Weight	Reps	Weight	Reps	Weight	Reps

WEDNESDAY	ocus area	Equipment	SET 1		SET 2		SET 3		SET 4	
			Weight	Reps	Weight	Reps	Weight	Reps	Weight	Reps

THURSDAY	ocus area	Equipment	SET 1		SET 2		SET 3		SET 4	
			Weight	Reps	Weight	Reps	Weight	Reps	Weight	Reps

FRIDAY	ocus area	Equipment	SET 1		SET 2		SET 3		SET 4	
			Weight	Reps	Weight	Reps	Weight	Reps	Weight	Reps

SATURDAY	ocus area	Equipment	SET 1		SET 2		SET 3		SET 4	
			Weight	Reps	Weight	Reps	Weight	Reps	Weight	Reps

SUNDAY	ocus area	Equipment	SET 1		SET 2		SET 3		SET 4	
			Weight	Reps	Weight	Reps	Weight	Reps	Weight	Reps

Cardio Training

MONDAY

Exercise	Time	Distance/ resistance	Intensity	Heart rate	Ease	Cal/kJ expended
						Total:

TUESDAY

Exercise	Time	Distance/ resistance	Intensity	Heart rate	Ease	Cal/kJ expended
						Total:

WEDNESDAY

Exercise	Time	Distance/ resistance	Intensity	Heart rate	Ease	Cal/kJ expended
						Total:

THURSDAY

Exercise	Time	Distance/ resistance	Intensity	Heart rate	Ease	Cal/kJ expended
						Total:

FRIDAY

Exercise	Time	Distance/ resistance	Intensity	Heart rate	Ease	Cal/kJ expended
						Total:

SATURDAY

Exercise	Time	Distance/ resistance	Intensity	Heart rate	Ease	Cal/kJ expended
						Total:

SUNDAY

Exercise	Time	Distance/ resistance	Intensity	Heart rate	Ease	Cal/kJ expended
						Total:
						Weekly Total:

Food Diary

MONDAY		Cal/kJ	Fat	Protein	Carbs
Breakfast time: am/pm					
Lunch time: am/pm					
Dinner time: am/pm					
Snacks:					
Coffees/teas:	Fluid intake: **Totals:**				

TUESDAY		Cal/kJ	Fat	Protein	Carbs
Breakfast time: am/pm					
Lunch time: am/pm					
Dinner time: am/pm					
Snacks:					
Coffees/teas:	Fluid intake: **Totals:**				

WEDNESDAY		Cal/kJ	Fat	Protein	Carbs
Breakfast time: am/pm					
Lunch time: am/pm					
Dinner time: am/pm					
Snacks:					
Coffees/teas:	Fluid intake: **Totals:**				

THURSDAY		Cal/kJ	Fat	Protein	Carbs
Breakfast time: am/pm					
Lunch time: am/pm					
Dinner time: am/pm					
Snacks:					
Coffees/teas:	Fluid intake: **Totals:**				

FRIDAY		Cal/kJ	Fat	Protein	Carbs
Breakfast time: am/pm					
Lunch time: am/pm					
Dinner time: am/pm					
Snacks:					
Coffees/teas:	Fluid intake: **Totals:**				

SATURDAY		Cal/kJ	Fat	Protein	Carbs
Breakfast time: am/pm					
Lunch time: am/pm					
Dinner time: am/pm					
Snacks:					
Coffees/teas:	Fluid intake: **Totals:**				

SUNDAY		Cal/kJ	Fat	Protein	Carbs
Breakfast time: am/pm					
Lunch time: am/pm					
Dinner time: am/pm					
Snacks:					
Coffees/teas:	Fluid intake: **Totals:**				

Units of alcohol this week: Total alcohol Cal/kJ:

Vitamins and supplements

Weekly Totals	Cal/kJ	Fat	Protein	Carbs

Weekly Personal Summary

Energy level 1–5

Stress level 1–5

Hours of sleep

Sleep quality 1–5

Mood 1–5

Appetite 1–5

Cal/kJ intake

Planned Cal/kJ	
Actual Cal/kJ	

Difference [+/-]

Weight at start of week

Weight at end of week

BMI at start of week

BMI at end of week

Injuries or illnesses

Week Beginning

/ /

Planned exercise sessions this week

	Exercise	Completed [Y/N]
Monday		
Tuesday		
Wednesday		
Thursday		
Friday		
Saturday		
Sunday		

Strength Training

MONDAY	Focus area	Equipment	SET 1		SET 2		SET 3		SET 4	
			Weight	Reps	Weight	Reps	Weight	Reps	Weight	Reps

TUESDAY	Focus area	Equipment	SET 1		SET 2		SET 3		SET 4	
			Weight	Reps	Weight	Reps	Weight	Reps	Weight	Reps

WEDNESDAY	Focus area	Equipment	SET 1		SET 2		SET 3		SET 4	
			Weight	Reps	Weight	Reps	Weight	Reps	Weight	Reps

THURSDAY	Focus area	Equipment	SET 1		SET 2		SET 3		SET 4	
			Weight	Reps	Weight	Reps	Weight	Reps	Weight	Reps

FRIDAY	Focus area	Equipment	SET 1		SET 2		SET 3		SET 4	
			Weight	Reps	Weight	Reps	Weight	Reps	Weight	Reps

SATURDAY	Focus area	Equipment	SET 1		SET 2		SET 3		SET 4	
			Weight	Reps	Weight	Reps	Weight	Reps	Weight	Reps

SUNDAY	Focus area	Equipment	SET 1		SET 2		SET 3		SET 4	
			Weight	Reps	Weight	Reps	Weight	Reps	Weight	Reps

Cardio Training

MONDAY

Exercise	Time	Distance/ resistance	Intensity	Heart rate	Ease	Cal/kJ expended
						Total:

TUESDAY

Exercise	Time	Distance/ resistance	Intensity	Heart rate	Ease	Cal/kJ expended
						Total:

WEDNESDAY

Exercise	Time	Distance/ resistance	Intensity	Heart rate	Ease	Cal/kJ expended
						Total:

THURSDAY

Exercise	Time	Distance/ resistance	Intensity	Heart rate	Ease	Cal/kJ expended
						Total:

FRIDAY

Exercise	Time	Distance/ resistance	Intensity	Heart rate	Ease	Cal/kJ expended
						Total:

SATURDAY

Exercise	Time	Distance/ resistance	Intensity	Heart rate	Ease	Cal/kJ expended
						Total:

SUNDAY

Exercise	Time	Distance/ resistance	Intensity	Heart rate	Ease	Cal/kJ expended
						Total:
						Weekly Total:

Food Diary

MONDAY			Cal/kJ	Fat	Protein	Carbs
Breakfast time: am/pm						
Lunch time: am/pm						
Dinner time: am/pm						
Snacks:						
Coffees/teas:	Fluid intake:	**Totals:**				

TUESDAY			Cal/kJ	Fat	Protein	Carbs
Breakfast time: am/pm						
Lunch time: am/pm						
Dinner time: am/pm						
Snacks:						
Coffees/teas:	Fluid intake:	**Totals:**				

WEDNESDAY			Cal/kJ	Fat	Protein	Carbs
Breakfast time: am/pm						
Lunch time: am/pm						
Dinner time: am/pm						
Snacks:						
Coffees/teas:	Fluid intake:	**Totals:**				

THURSDAY			Cal/kJ	Fat	Protein	Carbs
Breakfast time: am/pm						
Lunch time: am/pm						
Dinner time: am/pm						
Snacks:						
Coffees/teas:	Fluid intake:	**Totals:**				

FRIDAY		Cal/kJ	Fat	Protein	Carbs
Breakfast time: am/pm					
Lunch time: am/pm					
Dinner time: am/pm					
Snacks:					
Coffees/teas:	Fluid intake: **Totals:**				

SATURDAY		Cal/kJ	Fat	Protein	Carbs
Breakfast time: am/pm					
Lunch time: am/pm					
Dinner time: am/pm					
Snacks:					
Coffees/teas:	Fluid intake: **Totals:**				

SUNDAY		Cal/kJ	Fat	Protein	Carbs
Breakfast time: am/pm					
Lunch time: am/pm					
Dinner time: am/pm					
Snacks:					
Coffees/teas:	Fluid intake: **Totals:**				

Units of alcohol this week: Total alcohol Cal/kJ:

Vitamins and supplements

Weekly Totals	Cal/kJ	Fat	Protein	Carbs

Weekly Personal Summary

Energy level 1–5

Stress level 1–5

Hours of sleep

Sleep quality 1–5

Mood 1–5

Appetite 1–5

Cal/kJ intake

Planned Cal/kJ	
Actual Cal/kJ	
Difference [+/-]	

Weight at start of week

Weight at end of week

BMI at start of week

BMI at end of week

Injuries or illnesses

Week Beginning

/ /

Strength Training

Planned exercise sessions this week

	Exercise	Completed [Y/N]
Monday		
Tuesday		
Wednesday		
Thursday		
Friday		
Saturday		
Sunday		

MONDAY	Focus area	Equipment	SET 1		SET 2		SET 3		SET 4	
			Weight	Reps	Weight	Reps	Weight	Reps	Weight	Reps

TUESDAY	Focus area	Equipment	SET 1		SET 2		SET 3		SET 4	
			Weight	Reps	Weight	Reps	Weight	Reps	Weight	Reps

WEDNESDAY	Focus area	Equipment	SET 1		SET 2		SET 3		SET 4	
			Weight	Reps	Weight	Reps	Weight	Reps	Weight	Reps

THURSDAY	Focus area	Equipment	SET 1		SET 2		SET 3		SET 4	
			Weight	Reps	Weight	Reps	Weight	Reps	Weight	Reps

FRIDAY	Focus area	Equipment	SET 1		SET 2		SET 3		SET 4	
			Weight	Reps	Weight	Reps	Weight	Reps	Weight	Reps

SATURDAY	Focus area	Equipment	SET 1		SET 2		SET 3		SET 4	
			Weight	Reps	Weight	Reps	Weight	Reps	Weight	Reps

SUNDAY	Focus area	Equipment	SET 1		SET 2		SET 3		SET 4	
			Weight	Reps	Weight	Reps	Weight	Reps	Weight	Reps

Cardio Training

MONDAY

Exercise	Time	Distance/ resistance	Intensity	Heart rate	Ease	Cal/kJ expended
						Total:

TUESDAY

Exercise	Time	Distance/ resistance	Intensity	Heart rate	Ease	Cal/kJ expended
						Total:

WEDNESDAY

Exercise	Time	Distance/ resistance	Intensity	Heart rate	Ease	Cal/kJ expended
						Total:

THURSDAY

Exercise	Time	Distance/ resistance	Intensity	Heart rate	Ease	Cal/kJ expended
						Total:

FRIDAY

Exercise	Time	Distance/ resistance	Intensity	Heart rate	Ease	Cal/kJ expended
						Total:

SATURDAY

Exercise	Time	Distance/ resistance	Intensity	Heart rate	Ease	Cal/kJ expended
						Total:

SUNDAY

Exercise	Time	Distance/ resistance	Intensity	Heart rate	Ease	Cal/kJ expended
						Total:
					Weekly Total:	

Food Diary

MONDAY		Cal/kJ	Fat	Protein	Carbs
Breakfast time: am/pm					
Lunch time: am/pm					
Dinner time: am/pm					
Snacks:					
Coffees/teas: Fluid intake:	**Totals:**				

TUESDAY		Cal/kJ	Fat	Protein	Carbs
Breakfast time: am/pm					
Lunch time: am/pm					
Dinner time: am/pm					
Snacks:					
Coffees/teas: Fluid intake:	**Totals:**				

WEDNESDAY		Cal/kJ	Fat	Protein	Carbs
Breakfast time: am/pm					
Lunch time: am/pm					
Dinner time: am/pm					
Snacks:					
Coffees/teas: Fluid intake:	**Totals:**				

THURSDAY		Cal/kJ	Fat	Protein	Carbs
Breakfast time: am/pm					
Lunch time: am/pm					
Dinner time: am/pm					
Snacks:					
Coffees/teas: Fluid intake:	**Totals:**				

FRIDAY		Cal/kJ	Fat	Protein	Carbs
Breakfast time: am/pm					
Lunch time: am/pm					
Dinner time: am/pm					
Snacks:					
Coffees/teas:	Fluid intake: **Totals:**				

SATURDAY		Cal/kJ	Fat	Protein	Carbs
Breakfast time: am/pm					
Lunch time: am/pm					
Dinner time: am/pm					
Snacks:					
Coffees/teas:	Fluid intake: **Totals:**				

SUNDAY		Cal/kJ	Fat	Protein	Carbs
Breakfast time: am/pm					
Lunch time: am/pm					
Dinner time: am/pm					
Snacks:					
Coffees/teas:	Fluid intake: **Totals:**				

Units of alcohol this week: Total alcohol Cal/kJ:

Vitamins and supplements

Weekly Totals	Cal/kJ	Fat	Protein	Carbs

Weekly Personal Summary

Energy level (1–5) Stress level (1–5)

Hours of sleep Sleep quality (1–5)

Mood (1–5) Appetite (1–5)

Cal/kJ intake

Planned Cal/kJ

Actual Cal/kJ

Difference [+/-]

Weight at start of week

Weight at end of week

BMI at start of week

BMI at end of week

Injuries or illnesses

Week Beginning

/ /

Planned exercise sessions this week

	Exercise	Completed [Y/N]
Monday		
Tuesday		
Wednesday		
Thursday		
Friday		
Saturday		
Sunday		

Strength Training

	Focus area	Equipment	SET 1		SET 2		SET 3		SET 4	
			Weight	Reps	Weight	Reps	Weight	Reps	Weight	Reps
MONDAY										

	Focus area	Equipment	SET 1		SET 2		SET 3		SET 4	
			Weight	Reps	Weight	Reps	Weight	Reps	Weight	Reps
TUESDAY										

	Focus area	Equipment	SET 1		SET 2		SET 3		SET 4	
			Weight	Reps	Weight	Reps	Weight	Reps	Weight	Reps
WEDNESDAY										

	Focus area	Equipment	SET 1		SET 2		SET 3		SET 4	
			Weight	Reps	Weight	Reps	Weight	Reps	Weight	Reps
THURSDAY										

	Focus area	Equipment	SET 1		SET 2		SET 3		SET 4	
			Weight	Reps	Weight	Reps	Weight	Reps	Weight	Reps
FRIDAY										

	Focus area	Equipment	SET 1		SET 2		SET 3		SET 4	
			Weight	Reps	Weight	Reps	Weight	Reps	Weight	Reps
SATURDAY										

	Focus area	Equipment	SET 1		SET 2		SET 3		SET 4	
			Weight	Reps	Weight	Reps	Weight	Reps	Weight	Reps
SUNDAY										

Cardio Training

MONDAY

Exercise	Time	Distance/ resistance	Intensity	Heart rate	Ease	Cal/kJ expended
						Total:

TUESDAY

Exercise	Time	Distance/ resistance	Intensity	Heart rate	Ease	Cal/kJ expended
						Total:

WEDNESDAY

Exercise	Time	Distance/ resistance	Intensity	Heart rate	Ease	Cal/kJ expended
						Total:

THURSDAY

Exercise	Time	Distance/ resistance	Intensity	Heart rate	Ease	Cal/kJ expended
						Total:

FRIDAY

Exercise	Time	Distance/ resistance	Intensity	Heart rate	Ease	Cal/kJ expended
						Total:

SATURDAY

Exercise	Time	Distance/ resistance	Intensity	Heart rate	Ease	Cal/kJ expended
						Total:

SUNDAY

Exercise	Time	Distance/ resistance	Intensity	Heart rate	Ease	Cal/kJ expended
						Total:
						Weekly Total:

Food Diary

MONDAY			Cal/kJ	Fat	Protein	Carbs
Breakfast time: am/pm						
Lunch time: am/pm						
Dinner time: am/pm						
Snacks:						
Coffees/teas:	Fluid intake:	**Totals:**				

TUESDAY			Cal/kJ	Fat	Protein	Carbs
Breakfast time: am/pm						
Lunch time: am/pm						
Dinner time: am/pm						
Snacks:						
Coffees/teas:	Fluid intake:	**Totals:**				

WEDNESDAY			Cal/kJ	Fat	Protein	Carbs
Breakfast time: am/pm						
Lunch time: am/pm						
Dinner time: am/pm						
Snacks:						
Coffees/teas:	Fluid intake:	**Totals:**				

THURSDAY			Cal/kJ	Fat	Protein	Carbs
Breakfast time: am/pm						
Lunch time: am/pm						
Dinner time: am/pm						
Snacks:						
Coffees/teas:	Fluid intake:	**Totals:**				

FRIDAY		Cal/kJ	Fat	Protein	Carbs
Breakfast time: am/pm					
Lunch time: am/pm					
Dinner time: am/pm					
Snacks:					
Coffees/teas:	Fluid intake: **Totals:**				

SATURDAY		Cal/kJ	Fat	Protein	Carbs
Breakfast time: am/pm					
Lunch time: am/pm					
Dinner time: am/pm					
Snacks:					
Coffees/teas:	Fluid intake: **Totals:**				

SUNDAY		Cal/kJ	Fat	Protein	Carbs
Breakfast time: am/pm					
Lunch time: am/pm					
Dinner time: am/pm					
Snacks:					
Coffees/teas:	Fluid intake: **Totals:**				

Units of alcohol this week: Total alcohol Cal/kJ:

Vitamins and supplements

Weekly Totals	Cal/kJ	Fat	Protein	Carbs

Weekly Personal Summary

Energy level (1–5)

Stress level (1–5)

Hours of sleep

Sleep quality (1–5)

Mood (1–5)

Appetite (1–5)

Cal/kJ intake

Planned Cal/kJ	
Actual Cal/kJ	

Difference [+/-]

Weight at start of week

Weight at end of week

BMI at start of week

BMI at end of week

Injuries or illnesses

Week Beginning

/ /

Planned exercise sessions this week

	Exercise	Completed [Y/N]
Monday		
Tuesday		
Wednesday		
Thursday		
Friday		
Saturday		
Sunday		

Strength Training

MONDAY	ocus area	Equipment	SET 1		SET 2		SET 3		SET 4	
			Weight	Reps	Weight	Reps	Weight	Reps	Weight	Reps

TUESDAY	Focus area	Equipment	SET 1		SET 2		SET 3		SET 4	
			Weight	Reps	Weight	Reps	Weight	Reps	Weight	Reps

WEDNESDAY	ocus area	Equipment	SET 1		SET 2		SET 3		SET 4	
			Weight	Reps	Weight	Reps	Weight	Reps	Weight	Reps

THURSDAY	ocus area	Equipment	SET 1		SET 2		SET 3		SET 4	
			Weight	Reps	Weight	Reps	Weight	Reps	Weight	Reps

FRIDAY	Focus area	Equipment	SET 1		SET 2		SET 3		SET 4	
			Weight	Reps	Weight	Reps	Weight	Reps	Weight	Reps

SATURDAY	ocus area	Equipment	SET 1		SET 2		SET 3		SET 4	
			Weight	Reps	Weight	Reps	Weight	Reps	Weight	Reps

SUNDAY	Focus area	Equipment	SET 1		SET 2		SET 3		SET 4	
			Weight	Reps	Weight	Reps	Weight	Reps	Weight	Reps

Cardio Training

MONDAY	Exercise	Time	Distance/ resistance	Intensity	Heart rate	Ease	Cal/kJ expended
							Total:

TUESDAY	Exercise	Time	Distance/ resistance	Intensity	Heart rate	Ease	Cal/kJ expended
							Total:

WEDNESDAY	Exercise	Time	Distance/ resistance	Intensity	Heart rate	Ease	Cal/kJ expended
							Total:

THURSDAY	Exercise	Time	Distance/ resistance	Intensity	Heart rate	Ease	Cal/kJ expended
							Total:

FRIDAY	Exercise	Time	Distance/ resistance	Intensity	Heart rate	Ease	Cal/kJ expended
							Total:

SATURDAY	Exercise	Time	Distance/ resistance	Intensity	Heart rate	Ease	Cal/kJ expended
							Total:

SUNDAY	Exercise	Time	Distance/ resistance	Intensity	Heart rate	Ease	Cal/kJ expended
							Total:
							Weekly Total:

Food Diary

MONDAY			Cal/kJ	Fat	Protein	Carbs
Breakfast time: am/pm						
Lunch time: am/pm						
Dinner time: am/pm						
Snacks:						
Coffees/teas:	Fluid intake:	**Totals:**				

TUESDAY			Cal/kJ	Fat	Protein	Carbs
Breakfast time: am/pm						
Lunch time: am/pm						
Dinner time: am/pm						
Snacks:						
Coffees/teas:	Fluid intake:	**Totals:**				

WEDNESDAY			Cal/kJ	Fat	Protein	Carbs
Breakfast time: am/pm						
Lunch time: am/pm						
Dinner time: am/pm						
Snacks:						
Coffees/teas:	Fluid intake:	**Totals:**				

THURSDAY			Cal/kJ	Fat	Protein	Carbs
Breakfast time: am/pm						
Lunch time: am/pm						
Dinner time: am/pm						
Snacks:						
Coffees/teas:	Fluid intake:	**Totals:**				

FRIDAY		Cal/kJ	Fat	Protein	Carbs
Breakfast time: am/pm					
Lunch time: am/pm					
Dinner time: am/pm					
Snacks:					
Coffees/teas:	Fluid intake: **Totals:**				

SATURDAY		Cal/kJ	Fat	Protein	Carbs
Breakfast time: am/pm					
Lunch time: am/pm					
Dinner time: am/pm					
Snacks:					
Coffees/teas:	Fluid intake: **Totals:**				

SUNDAY		Cal/kJ	Fat	Protein	Carbs
Breakfast time: am/pm					
Lunch time: am/pm					
Dinner time: am/pm					
Snacks:					
Coffees/teas:	Fluid intake: **Totals:**				

Units of alcohol this week: Total alcohol Cal/kJ:

Vitamins and supplements

	Cal/kJ	Fat	Protein	Carbs
Weekly Totals				

Weekly Personal Summary

Energy level (1–5) Stress level (1–5)

Hours of sleep Sleep quality (1–5)

Mood (1–5) Appetite (1–5)

Cal/kJ intake

Planned Cal/kJ	
Actual Cal/kJ	
Difference [+/-]	

Weight at start of week

Weight at end of week

BMI at start of week

BMI at end of week

Injuries or illnesses

Monthly Summary

MONTH 1

DATE / / AGE HEIGHT

Physical Measurements		
Last Mth's Target		This Mth's Result
	Weight	
	BMI	
	Waist–hip ratio	
	Chest, relaxed	
	Chest, expanded	
	Waist	
	Stomach	
	Hips	
	Neck	
	Shoulders	
	Right upper arm, relaxed	
	Right upper arm, flexed	
	Left upper arm, relaxed	
	Left upper arm, flexed	
	Right forearm, relaxed	
	Right forearm, flexed	
	Left forearm, relaxed	
	Left forearm, flexed	
	Right upper thigh	
	Right lower thigh	
	Left upper thigh	
	Left lower thigh	
	Right calf	
	Left calf	

Total your weekly results and divide by the number of weeks to get your average.

Average monthly mood (1–5)

Average monthly appetite (1–5)

Average monthly energy level (1–5)

Average monthly stress level (1–5)

Average weekly hours of sleep

Average monthly sleep quality (1–5)

Number of planned exercise sessions this month

Number of completed exercise sessions this month

Average daily coffees/ teas

Average daily fluid intake

Average weekly units of alcohol

Cardiovascular Fitness Test					
		Last Month	Target	Actual	Next Mth's Target
Resting heart rate					
Working heart rate:	after 3 minutes				
	after 6 minutes				
	after 9 minutes				
Recovery heart rate:	at course completion				
	1 minute after completion				
	2 minutes after completion				
	3 minutes after completion				
Completion time					

Endurance				
	Last Month	Target	Actual	Next Mth's Target
Time to run 1 mile/2km				
Number of push-ups before you have to stop				
Number of sit-ups before you have to stop				
Number of squats before you have to stop				
Number of inches/cm you can stretch up to or beyond your feet (+/-)				
Time you can balance on one foot: right leg left leg				

Total your daily dietary results and divide by the number of days in the month to get your daily average.

Average Daily Dietary Results			
	Target	Result	Difference [+/-]
Fat intake			
Cal/kJ intake			
Carbs intake			
Protein intake			

Next Month's Targets

Physical Measurement Targets			
	Next Mth's Target		Next Mth's Target
Weight		Left upper arm, relaxed	
BMI		Left upper arm, flexed	
Waist–hip ratio		Right forearm, relaxed	
Chest, relaxed		Right forearm, flexed	
Chest, expanded		Left forearm, relaxed	
Waist		Left forearm, flexed	
Stomach		Right upper thigh	
Hips		Right lower thigh	
Neck		Left upper thigh	
Shoulders		Left lower thigh	
Right upper arm, relaxed		Right calf	
Right upper arm, flexed		Left calf	

Average Daily Dietary Targets			
	Next Mth's Target		Next Mth's Target
Fat		Daily fluid intake	
Cal/kJ		Daily coffee/tea intake	
Protein		Weekly alcohol intake	
Carbs			

Monthly Summary

MONTH 2 DATE / / AGE HEIGHT

Physical Measurements		
Last Mth's Target		This Mth's Result
	Weight	
	BMI	
	Waist–hip ratio	
	Chest, relaxed	
	Chest, expanded	
	Waist	
	Stomach	
	Hips	
	Neck	
	Shoulders	
	Right upper arm, relaxed	
	Right upper arm, flexed	
	Left upper arm, relaxed	
	Left upper arm, flexed	
	Right forearm, relaxed	
	Right forearm, flexed	
	Left forearm, relaxed	
	Left forearm, flexed	
	Right upper thigh	
	Right lower thigh	
	Left upper thigh	
	Left lower thigh	
	Right calf	
	Left calf	

Total your weekly results and divide by the number of weeks to get your average.

Average monthly mood 1–5

Average monthly appetite 1–5

Average monthly energy level 1–5

Average monthly stress level 1–5

Average weekly hours of sleep

Average monthly sleep quality 1–5

Number of planned exercise sessions this month

Number of completed exercise sessions this month

Average daily coffees/ teas

Average daily fluid intake

Average weekly units of alcohol

Cardiovascular Fitness Test		Last Month	Target	Actual	Next Mth's Target
Resting heart rate					
Working heart rate:	after 3 minutes				
	after 6 minutes				
	after 9 minutes				
Recovery heart rate:	at course completion				
	1 minute after completion				
	2 minutes after completion				
	3 minutes after completion				
Completion time					

Endurance				
	Last Month	Target	Actual	Next Mth's Target
Time to run 1 mile/2km				
Number of push-ups before you have to stop				
Number of sit-ups before you have to stop				
Number of squats before you have to stop				
Number of inches/cm you can stretch up to or beyond your feet (+/-)				
Time you can balance on one foot: right leg left leg				

Total your daily dietary results and divide by the number of days in the month to get your daily average.

Average Daily Dietary Results			
	Target	Result	Difference [+/-]
Fat intake			
Cal/kJ intake			
Carbs intake			
Protein intake			

Next Month's Targets

Physical Measurement Targets			
	Next Mth's Target		Next Mth's Target
Weight		Left upper arm, relaxed	
BMI		Left upper arm, flexed	
Waist–hip ratio		Right forearm, relaxed	
Chest, relaxed		Right forearm, flexed	
Chest, expanded		Left forearm, relaxed	
Waist		Left forearm, flexed	
Stomach		Right upper thigh	
Hips		Right lower thigh	
Neck		Left upper thigh	
Shoulders		Left lower thigh	
Right upper arm, relaxed		Right calf	
Right upper arm, flexed		Left calf	

Average Daily Dietary Targets			
	Next Mth's Target		Next Mth's Target
Fat		Daily fluid intake	
Cal/kJ		Daily coffee/tea intake	
Protein		Weekly alcohol intake	
Carbs			

Monthly Summary

MONTH 3 DATE / / AGE HEIGHT

Physical Measurements		
Last Mth's Target		This Mth's Result
	Weight	
	BMI	
	Waist–hip ratio	
	Chest, relaxed	
	Chest, expanded	
	Waist	
	Stomach	
	Hips	
	Neck	
	Shoulders	
	Right upper arm, relaxed	
	Right upper arm, flexed	
	Left upper arm, relaxed	
	Left upper arm, flexed	
	Right forearm, relaxed	
	Right forearm, flexed	
	Left forearm, relaxed	
	Left forearm, flexed	
	Right upper thigh	
	Right lower thigh	
	Left upper thigh	
	Left lower thigh	
	Right calf	
	Left calf	

Total your weekly results and divide by the number of weeks to get your average.

Average monthly mood 1–5

Average monthly appetite 1–5

Average monthly energy level 1–5

Average monthly stress level 1–5

Average weekly hours of sleep

Average monthly sleep quality 1–5

Number of planned exercise sessions this month

Number of completed exercise sessions this month

Average daily coffees/ teas

Average daily fluid intake

Average weekly units of alcohol

Cardiovascular Fitness Test		Last Month	Target	Actual	Next Mth's Target
Resting heart rate					
Working heart rate:	after 3 minutes				
	after 6 minutes				
	after 9 minutes				
Recovery heart rate:	at course completion				
	1 minute after completion				
	2 minutes after completion				
	3 minutes after completion				
Completion time					

Endurance				
	Last Month	Target	Actual	Next Mth's Target
Time to run 1 mile/2km				
Number of push-ups before you have to stop				
Number of sit-ups before you have to stop				
Number of squats before you have to stop				
Number of inches/cm you can stretch up to or beyond your feet (+/-)				
Time you can balance on one foot: right leg left leg				

Total your daily dietary results and divide by the number of days in the month to get your daily average.

Average Daily Dietary Results			
	Target	Result	Difference [+/-]
Fat intake			
Cal/kJ intake			
Carbs intake			
Protein intake			

Next Month's Targets

Physical Measurement Targets			
	Next Mth's Target		Next Mth's Target
Weight		Left upper arm, relaxed	
BMI		Left upper arm, flexed	
Waist–hip ratio		Right forearm, relaxed	
Chest, relaxed		Right forearm, flexed	
Chest, expanded		Left forearm, relaxed	
Waist		Left forearm, flexed	
Stomach		Right upper thigh	
Hips		Right lower thigh	
Neck		Left upper thigh	
Shoulders		Left lower thigh	
Right upper arm, relaxed		Right calf	
Right upper arm, flexed		Left calf	

Average Daily Dietary Targets			
	Next Mth's Target		Next Mth's Target
Fat		Daily fluid intake	
Cal/kJ		Daily coffee/tea intake	
Protein		Weekly alcohol intake	
Carbs			

Monthly Summary

MONTH 4

DATE / / AGE HEIGHT

Physical Measurements		
Last Mth's Target		This Mth's Result
	Weight	
	BMI	
	Waist–hip ratio	
	Chest, relaxed	
	Chest, expanded	
	Waist	
	Stomach	
	Hips	
	Neck	
	Shoulders	
	Right upper arm, relaxed	
	Right upper arm, flexed	
	Left upper arm, relaxed	
	Left upper arm, flexed	
	Right forearm, relaxed	
	Right forearm, flexed	
	Left forearm, relaxed	
	Left forearm, flexed	
	Right upper thigh	
	Right lower thigh	
	Left upper thigh	
	Left lower thigh	
	Right calf	
	Left calf	

Total your weekly results and divide by the number of weeks to get your average.

Average monthly mood (1–5)

Average monthly appetite (1–5)

Average monthly energy level (1–5)

Average monthly stress level (1–5)

Average weekly hours of sleep

Average monthly sleep quality (1–5)

Number of planned exercise sessions this month

Number of completed exercise sessions this month

Average daily coffees/ teas

Average daily fluid intake

Average weekly units of alcohol

Cardiovascular Fitness Test		Last Month	Target	Actual	Next Mth's Target
Resting heart rate					
Working heart rate:	after 3 minutes				
	after 6 minutes				
	after 9 minutes				
Recovery heart rate:	at course completion				
	1 minute after completion				
	2 minutes after completion				
	3 minutes after completion				
Completion time					

Endurance				
	Last Month	Target	Actual	Next Mth's Target
Time to run 1 mile/2km				
Number of push-ups before you have to stop				
Number of sit-ups before you have to stop				
Number of squats before you have to stop				
Number of inches/cm you can stretch up to or beyond your feet (+/-)				
Time you can balance on one foot: right leg left leg				

Total your daily dietary results and divide by the number of days in the month to get your daily average.

Average Daily Dietary Results			
	Target	Result	Difference [+/-]
Fat intake			
Cal/kJ intake			
Carbs intake			
Protein intake			

Next Month's Targets

Physical Measurement Targets			
	Next Mth's Target		Next Mth's Target
Weight		Left upper arm, relaxed	
BMI		Left upper arm, flexed	
Waist–hip ratio		Right forearm, relaxed	
Chest, relaxed		Right forearm, flexed	
Chest, expanded		Left forearm, relaxed	
Waist		Left forearm, flexed	
Stomach		Right upper thigh	
Hips		Right lower thigh	
Neck		Left upper thigh	
Shoulders		Left lower thigh	
Right upper arm, relaxed		Right calf	
Right upper arm, flexed		Left calf	

Average Daily Dietary Targets			
	Next Mth's Target		Next Mth's Target
Fat		Daily fluid intake	
Cal/kJ		Daily coffee/tea intake	
Protein		Weekly alcohol intake	
Carbs			

Monthly Summary

MONTH 5 DATE / / AGE HEIGHT

Physical Measurements		
Last Mth's Target		This Mth's Result
	Weight	
	BMI	
	Waist–hip ratio	
	Chest, relaxed	
	Chest, expanded	
	Waist	
	Stomach	
	Hips	
	Neck	
	Shoulders	
	Right upper arm, relaxed	
	Right upper arm, flexed	
	Left upper arm, relaxed	
	Left upper arm, flexed	
	Right forearm, relaxed	
	Right forearm, flexed	
	Left forearm, relaxed	
	Left forearm, flexed	
	Right upper thigh	
	Right lower thigh	
	Left upper thigh	
	Left lower thigh	
	Right calf	
	Left calf	

Total your weekly results and divide by the number of weeks to get your average.

Average monthly mood 1–5

Average monthly appetite 1–5

Average monthly energy level 1–5

Average monthly stress level 1–5

Average weekly hours of sleep

Average monthly sleep quality 1–5

Number of planned exercise sessions this month

Number of completed exercise sessions this month

Average daily coffees/teas

Average daily fluid intake

Average weekly units of alcohol

Cardiovascular Fitness Test		Last Month	Target	Actual	Next Mth's Target
Resting heart rate					
Working heart rate:	after 3 minutes				
	after 6 minutes				
	after 9 minutes				
Recovery heart rate:	at course completion				
	1 minute after completion				
	2 minutes after completion				
	3 minutes after completion				
Completion time					

Endurance				
	Last Month	Target	Actual	Next Mth's Target
Time to run 1 mile/2km				
Number of push-ups before you have to stop				
Number of sit-ups before you have to stop				
Number of squats before you have to stop				
Number of inches/cm you can stretch up to or beyond your feet (+/-)				
Time you can balance on one foot: right leg left leg				

Total your daily dietary results and divide by the number of days in the month to get your daily average.

Average Daily Dietary Results			
	Target	Result	Difference [+/-]
Fat intake			
Cal/kJ intake			
Carbs intake			
Protein intake			

Next Month's Targets

Physical Measurement Targets			
	Next Mth's Target		Next Mth's Target
Weight		Left upper arm, relaxed	
BMI		Left upper arm, flexed	
Waist–hip ratio		Right forearm, relaxed	
Chest, relaxed		Right forearm, flexed	
Chest, expanded		Left forearm, relaxed	
Waist		Left forearm, flexed	
Stomach		Right upper thigh	
Hips		Right lower thigh	
Neck		Left upper thigh	
Shoulders		Left lower thigh	
Right upper arm, relaxed		Right calf	
Right upper arm, flexed		Left calf	

Average Daily Dietary Targets			
	Next Mth's Target		Next Mth's Target
Fat		Daily fluid intake	
Cal/kJ		Daily coffee/tea intake	
Protein		Weekly alcohol intake	
Carbs			

Monthly Summary

MONTH 6

DATE / / AGE HEIGHT

Last Mth's Target	Physical Measurements	This Mth's Result
	Weight	
	BMI	
	Waist–hip ratio	
	Chest, relaxed	
	Chest, expanded	
	Waist	
	Stomach	
	Hips	
	Neck	
	Shoulders	
	Right upper arm, relaxed	
	Right upper arm, flexed	
	Left upper arm, relaxed	
	Left upper arm, flexed	
	Right forearm, relaxed	
	Right forearm, flexed	
	Left forearm, relaxed	
	Left forearm, flexed	
	Right upper thigh	
	Right lower thigh	
	Left upper thigh	
	Left lower thigh	
	Right calf	
	Left calf	

Total your weekly results and divide by the number of weeks to get your average.

Average monthly mood	1–5	
Average monthly appetite	1–5	
Average monthly energy level	1–5	
Average monthly stress level	1–5	
Average weekly hours of sleep		
Average monthly sleep quality	1–5	
Number of planned exercise sessions this month		
Number of completed exercise sessions this month		
Average daily coffees/teas		
Average daily fluid intake		
Average weekly units of alcohol		

Cardiovascular Fitness Test

		Last Month	Target	Actual	Next Mth's Target
Resting heart rate					
Working heart rate:	after 3 minutes				
	after 6 minutes				
	after 9 minutes				
Recovery heart rate:	at course completion				
	1 minute after completion				
	2 minutes after completion				
	3 minutes after completion				
Completion time					

Endurance				
	Last Month	Target	Actual	Next Mth's Target
Time to run 1 mile/2km				
Number of push-ups before you have to stop				
Number of sit-ups before you have to stop				
Number of squats before you have to stop				
Number of inches/cm you can stretch up to or beyond your feet (+/-)				
Time you can balance on one foot: right leg left leg				

Total your daily dietary results and divide by the number of days in the month to get your daily average.

Average Daily Dietary Results			
	Target	Result	Difference [+/-]
Fat intake			
Cal/kJ intake			
Carbs intake			
Protein intake			

Next Month's Targets

Physical Measurement Targets			
	Next Mth's Target		Next Mth's Target
Weight		Left upper arm, relaxed	
BMI		Left upper arm, flexed	
Waist–hip ratio		Right forearm, relaxed	
Chest, relaxed		Right forearm, flexed	
Chest, expanded		Left forearm, relaxed	
Waist		Left forearm, flexed	
Stomach		Right upper thigh	
Hips		Right lower thigh	
Neck		Left upper thigh	
Shoulders		Left lower thigh	
Right upper arm, relaxed		Right calf	
Right upper arm, flexed		Left calf	

Average Daily Dietary Targets			
	Next Mth's Target		Next Mth's Target
Fat		Daily fluid intake	
Cal/kJ		Daily coffee/tea intake	
Protein		Weekly alcohol intake	
Carbs			

Monthly Summary

MONTH 7 DATE / / AGE HEIGHT

Physical Measurements		
Last Mth's Target		This Mth's Result
	Weight	
	BMI	
	Waist–hip ratio	
	Chest, relaxed	
	Chest, expanded	
	Waist	
	Stomach	
	Hips	
	Neck	
	Shoulders	
	Right upper arm, relaxed	
	Right upper arm, flexed	
	Left upper arm, relaxed	
	Left upper arm, flexed	
	Right forearm, relaxed	
	Right forearm, flexed	
	Left forearm, relaxed	
	Left forearm, flexed	
	Right upper thigh	
	Right lower thigh	
	Left upper thigh	
	Left lower thigh	
	Right calf	
	Left calf	

Total your weekly results and divide by the number of weeks to get your average.

Average monthly mood	1–5
Average monthly appetite	1–5
Average monthly energy level	1–5
Average monthly stress level	1–5
Average weekly hours of sleep	
Average monthly sleep quality	1–5
Number of planned exercise sessions this month	
Number of completed exercise sessions this month	
Average daily coffees/teas	
Average daily fluid intake	
Average weekly units of alcohol	

Cardiovascular Fitness Test					
		Last Month	Target	Actual	Next Mth's Target
Resting heart rate					
Working heart rate:	after 3 minutes				
	after 6 minutes				
	after 9 minutes				
Recovery heart rate:	at course completion				
	1 minute after completion				
	2 minutes after completion				
	3 minutes after completion				
Completion time					

Endurance				
	Last Month	Target	Actual	Next Mth's Target
Time to run 1 mile/2km				
Number of push-ups before you have to stop				
Number of sit-ups before you have to stop				
Number of squats before you have to stop				
Number of inches/cm you can stretch up to or beyond your feet (+/-)				
Time you can balance on one foot: right leg left leg				

Total your daily dietary results and divide by the number of days in the month to get your daily average.

Average Daily Dietary Results			
	Target	Result	Difference [+/-]
Fat intake			
Cal/kJ intake			
Carbs intake			
Protein intake			

Next Month's Targets

Physical Measurement Targets			
	Next Mth's Target		Next Mth's Target
Weight		Left upper arm, relaxed	
BMI		Left upper arm, flexed	
Waist–hip ratio		Right forearm, relaxed	
Chest, relaxed		Right forearm, flexed	
Chest, expanded		Left forearm, relaxed	
Waist		Left forearm, flexed	
Stomach		Right upper thigh	
Hips		Right lower thigh	
Neck		Left upper thigh	
Shoulders		Left lower thigh	
Right upper arm, relaxed		Right calf	
Right upper arm, flexed		Left calf	

Average Daily Dietary Targets			
	Next Mth's Target		Next Mth's Target
Fat		Daily fluid intake	
Cal/kJ		Daily coffee/tea intake	
Protein		Weekly alcohol intake	
Carbs			

Monthly Summary

MONTH 8 DATE / / AGE HEIGHT

Last Mth's Target	Physical Measurements	This Mth's Result
	Weight	
	BMI	
	Waist–hip ratio	
	Chest, relaxed	
	Chest, expanded	
	Waist	
	Stomach	
	Hips	
	Neck	
	Shoulders	
	Right upper arm, relaxed	
	Right upper arm, flexed	
	Left upper arm, relaxed	
	Left upper arm, flexed	
	Right forearm, relaxed	
	Right forearm, flexed	
	Left forearm, relaxed	
	Left forearm, flexed	
	Right upper thigh	
	Right lower thigh	
	Left upper thigh	
	Left lower thigh	
	Right calf	
	Left calf	

Total your weekly results and divide by the number of weeks to get your average.

Average monthly mood	1–5
Average monthly appetite	1–5
Average monthly energy level	1–5
Average monthly stress level	1–5
Average weekly hours of sleep	
Average monthly sleep quality	1–5
Number of planned exercise sessions this month	
Number of completed exercise sessions this month	
Average daily coffees/ teas	
Average daily fluid intake	
Average weekly units of alcohol	

Cardiovascular Fitness Test

		Last Month	Target	Actual	Next Mth's Target
Resting heart rate					
Working heart rate:	after 3 minutes				
	after 6 minutes				
	after 9 minutes				
Recovery heart rate:	at course completion				
	1 minute after completion				
	2 minutes after completion				
	3 minutes after completion				
Completion time					

Endurance				
	Last Month	Target	Actual	Next Mth's Target
Time to run 1 mile/2km				
Number of push-ups before you have to stop				
Number of sit-ups before you have to stop				
Number of squats before you have to stop				
Number of inches/cm you can stretch up to or beyond your feet (+/-)				
Time you can balance on one foot: right leg left leg				

Total your daily dietary results and divide by the number of days in the month to get your daily average.

Average Daily Dietary Results			
	Target	Result	Difference [+/-]
Fat intake			
Cal/kJ intake			
Carbs intake			
Protein intake			

Next Month's Targets

Physical Measurement Targets			
	Next Mth's Target		Next Mth's Target
Weight		Left upper arm, relaxed	
BMI		Left upper arm, flexed	
Waist–hip ratio		Right forearm, relaxed	
Chest, relaxed		Right forearm, flexed	
Chest, expanded		Left forearm, relaxed	
Waist		Left forearm, flexed	
Stomach		Right upper thigh	
Hips		Right lower thigh	
Neck		Left upper thigh	
Shoulders		Left lower thigh	
Right upper arm, relaxed		Right calf	
Right upper arm, flexed		Left calf	

Average Daily Dietary Targets			
	Next Mth's Target		Next Mth's Target
Fat		Daily fluid intake	
Cal/kJ		Daily coffee/tea intake	
Protein		Weekly alcohol intake	
Carbs			

Monthly Summary

MONTH 9 DATE / / AGE HEIGHT

Last Mth's Target	Physical Measurements	This Mth's Result
	Weight	
	BMI	
	Waist–hip ratio	
	Chest, relaxed	
	Chest, expanded	
	Waist	
	Stomach	
	Hips	
	Neck	
	Shoulders	
	Right upper arm, relaxed	
	Right upper arm, flexed	
	Left upper arm, relaxed	
	Left upper arm, flexed	
	Right forearm, relaxed	
	Right forearm, flexed	
	Left forearm, relaxed	
	Left forearm, flexed	
	Right upper thigh	
	Right lower thigh	
	Left upper thigh	
	Left lower thigh	
	Right calf	
	Left calf	

Total your weekly results and divide by the number of weeks to get your average.

Average monthly mood (1–5)

Average monthly appetite (1–5)

Average monthly energy level (1–5)

Average monthly stress level (1–5)

Average weekly hours of sleep

Average monthly sleep quality (1–5)

Number of planned exercise sessions this month

Number of completed exercise sessions this month

Average daily coffees/ teas

Average daily fluid intake

Average weekly units of alcohol

Cardiovascular Fitness Test

		Last Month	Target	Actual	Next Mth's Target
Resting heart rate					
Working heart rate:	after 3 minutes				
	after 6 minutes				
	after 9 minutes				
Recovery heart rate:	at course completion				
	1 minute after completion				
	2 minutes after completion				
	3 minutes after completion				
Completion time					

Endurance				
	Last Month	Target	Actual	Next Mth's Target
Time to run 1 mile/2km				
Number of push-ups before you have to stop				
Number of sit-ups before you have to stop				
Number of squats before you have to stop				
Number of inches/cm you can stretch up to or beyond your feet (+/-)				
Time you can balance on one foot: right leg left leg				

Total your daily dietary results and divide by the number of days in the month to get your daily average.

Average Daily Dietary Results			
	Target	Result	Difference [+/-]
Fat intake			
Cal/kJ intake			
Carbs intake			
Protein intake			

Next Month's Targets

Physical Measurement Targets			
	Next Mth's Target		Next Mth's Target
Weight		Left upper arm, relaxed	
BMI		Left upper arm, flexed	
Waist–hip ratio		Right forearm, relaxed	
Chest, relaxed		Right forearm, flexed	
Chest, expanded		Left forearm, relaxed	
Waist		Left forearm, flexed	
Stomach		Right upper thigh	
Hips		Right lower thigh	
Neck		Left upper thigh	
Shoulders		Left lower thigh	
Right upper arm, relaxed		Right calf	
Right upper arm, flexed		Left calf	

Average Daily Dietary Targets			
	Next Mth's Target		Next Mth's Target
Fat		Daily fluid intake	
Cal/kJ		Daily coffee/tea intake	
Protein		Weekly alcohol intake	
Carbs			

Monthly Summary

MONTH 10 DATE / / AGE HEIGHT

Physical Measurements		
Last Mth's Target		This Mth's Result
	Weight	
	BMI	
	Waist–hip ratio	
	Chest, relaxed	
	Chest, expanded	
	Waist	
	Stomach	
	Hips	
	Neck	
	Shoulders	
	Right upper arm, relaxed	
	Right upper arm, flexed	
	Left upper arm, relaxed	
	Left upper arm, flexed	
	Right forearm, relaxed	
	Right forearm, flexed	
	Left forearm, relaxed	
	Left forearm, flexed	
	Right upper thigh	
	Right lower thigh	
	Left upper thigh	
	Left lower thigh	
	Right calf	
	Left calf	

Total your weekly results and divide by the number of weeks to get your average.

Average monthly mood 1–5

Average monthly appetite 1–5

Average monthly energy level 1–5

Average monthly stress level 1–5

Average weekly hours of sleep

Average monthly sleep quality 1–5

Number of planned exercise sessions this month

Number of completed exercise sessions this month

Average daily coffees/teas

Average daily fluid intake

Average weekly units of alcohol

Cardiovascular Fitness Test					
		Last Month	Target	Actual	Next Mth's Target
Resting heart rate					
Working heart rate:	after 3 minutes				
	after 6 minutes				
	after 9 minutes				
Recovery heart rate:	at course completion				
	1 minute after completion				
	2 minutes after completion				
	3 minutes after completion				
Completion time					

Endurance				
	Last Month	Target	Actual	Next Mth's Target
Time to run 1 mile/2km				
Number of push-ups before you have to stop				
Number of sit-ups before you have to stop				
Number of squats before you have to stop				
Number of inches/cm you can stretch up to or beyond your feet (+/-)				
Time you can balance on one foot: right leg left leg				

Total your daily dietary results and divide by the number of days in the month to get your daily average.

Average Daily Dietary Results			
	Target	Result	Difference [+/-]
Fat intake			
Cal/kJ intake			
Carbs intake			
Protein intake			

Next Month's Targets

Physical Measurement Targets			
	Next Mth's Target		Next Mth's Target
Weight		Left upper arm, relaxed	
BMI		Left upper arm, flexed	
Waist–hip ratio		Right forearm, relaxed	
Chest, relaxed		Right forearm, flexed	
Chest, expanded		Left forearm, relaxed	
Waist		Left forearm, flexed	
Stomach		Right upper thigh	
Hips		Right lower thigh	
Neck		Left upper thigh	
Shoulders		Left lower thigh	
Right upper arm, relaxed		Right calf	
Right upper arm, flexed		Left calf	

Average Daily Dietary Targets			
	Next Mth's Target		Next Mth's Target
Fat		Daily fluid intake	
Cal/kJ		Daily coffee/tea intake	
Protein		Weekly alcohol intake	
Carbs			

Monthly Summary

MONTH 11 DATE / / AGE HEIGHT

Last Mth's Target	Physical Measurements	This Mth's Result
	Weight	
	BMI	
	Waist–hip ratio	
	Chest, relaxed	
	Chest, expanded	
	Waist	
	Stomach	
	Hips	
	Neck	
	Shoulders	
	Right upper arm, relaxed	
	Right upper arm, flexed	
	Left upper arm, relaxed	
	Left upper arm, flexed	
	Right forearm, relaxed	
	Right forearm, flexed	
	Left forearm, relaxed	
	Left forearm, flexed	
	Right upper thigh	
	Right lower thigh	
	Left upper thigh	
	Left lower thigh	
	Right calf	
	Left calf	

Total your weekly results and divide by the number of weeks to get your average.

Average monthly mood 1–5

Average monthly appetite 1–5

Average monthly energy level 1–5

Average monthly stress level 1–5

Average weekly hours of sleep

Average monthly sleep quality 1–5

Number of planned exercise sessions this month

Number of completed exercise sessions this month

Average daily coffees/teas

Average daily fluid intake

Average weekly units of alcohol

Cardiovascular Fitness Test

		Last Month	Target	Actual	Next Mth's Target
Resting heart rate					
Working heart rate:	after 3 minutes				
	after 6 minutes				
	after 9 minutes				
Recovery heart rate:	at course completion				
	1 minute after completion				
	2 minutes after completion				
	3 minutes after completion				
Completion time					

Endurance				
	Last Month	Target	Actual	Next Mth's Target
Time to run 1 mile/2km				
Number of push-ups before you have to stop				
Number of sit-ups before you have to stop				
Number of squats before you have to stop				
Number of inches/cm you can stretch up to or beyond your feet (+/-)				
Time you can balance on one foot: right leg left leg				

Total your daily dietary results and divide by the number of days in the month to get your daily average.

Average Daily Dietary Results			
	Target	Result	Difference [+/-]
Fat intake			
Cal/kJ intake			
Carbs intake			
Protein intake			

Next Month's Targets

Physical Measurement Targets			
	Next Mth's Target		Next Mth's Target
Weight		Left upper arm, relaxed	
BMI		Left upper arm, flexed	
Waist–hip ratio		Right forearm, relaxed	
Chest, relaxed		Right forearm, flexed	
Chest, expanded		Left forearm, relaxed	
Waist		Left forearm, flexed	
Stomach		Right upper thigh	
Hips		Right lower thigh	
Neck		Left upper thigh	
Shoulders		Left lower thigh	
Right upper arm, relaxed		Right calf	
Right upper arm, flexed		Left calf	

Average Daily Dietary Targets			
	Next Mth's Target		Next Mth's Target
Fat		Daily fluid intake	
Cal/kJ		Daily coffee/tea intake	
Protein		Weekly alcohol intake	
Carbs			

Monthly Summary

MONTH 12 DATE / / AGE HEIGHT

Physical Measurements		
Last Mth's Target		This Mth's Result
	Weight	
	BMI	
	Waist–hip ratio	
	Chest, relaxed	
	Chest, expanded	
	Waist	
	Stomach	
	Hips	
	Neck	
	Shoulders	
	Right upper arm, relaxed	
	Right upper arm, flexed	
	Left upper arm, relaxed	
	Left upper arm, flexed	
	Right forearm, relaxed	
	Right forearm, flexed	
	Left forearm, relaxed	
	Left forearm, flexed	
	Right upper thigh	
	Right lower thigh	
	Left upper thigh	
	Left lower thigh	
	Right calf	
	Left calf	

Total your weekly results and divide by the number of weeks to get your average.

Average monthly mood 1–5

Average monthly appetite 1–5

Average monthly energy level 1–5

Average monthly stress level 1–5

Average weekly hours of sleep

Average monthly sleep quality 1–5

Number of planned exercise sessions this month

Number of completed exercise sessions this month

Average daily coffees/ teas

Average daily fluid intake

Average weekly units of alcohol

Cardiovascular Fitness Test					
		Last Month	Target	Actual	Next Mth's Target
Resting heart rate					
Working heart rate:	after 3 minutes				
	after 6 minutes				
	after 9 minutes				
Recovery heart rate:	at course completion				
	1 minute after completion				
	2 minutes after completion				
	3 minutes after completion				
Completion time					

Endurance				
	Last Month	Target	Actual	Next Mth's Target
Time to run 1 mile/2km				
Number of push-ups before you have to stop				
Number of sit-ups before you have to stop				
Number of squats before you have to stop				
Number of inches/cm you can stretch up to or beyond your feet (+/-)				
Time you can balance on one foot: right leg left leg				

Total your daily dietary results and divide by the number of days in the month to get your daily average.

Average Daily Dietary Results			
	Target	Result	Difference [+/-]
Fat intake			
Cal/kJ intake			
Carbs intake			
Protein intake			

Next Month's Targets

Physical Measurement Targets			
	Next Mth's Target		Next Mth's Target
Weight		Left upper arm, relaxed	
BMI		Left upper arm, flexed	
Waist–hip ratio		Right forearm, relaxed	
Chest, relaxed		Right forearm, flexed	
Chest, expanded		Left forearm, relaxed	
Waist		Left forearm, flexed	
Stomach		Right upper thigh	
Hips		Right lower thigh	
Neck		Left upper thigh	
Shoulders		Left lower thigh	
Right upper arm, relaxed		Right calf	
Right upper arm, flexed		Left calf	

Average Daily Dietary Targets			
	Next Mth's Target		Next Mth's Target
Fat		Daily fluid intake	
Cal/kJ		Daily coffee/tea intake	
Protein		Weekly alcohol intake	
Carbs			

End-of-Year Assessment

DATE   /   /   AGE   HEIGHT

Physical Measurement Targets		Actual Physical Measurement Results		Difference [+/-]
Weight		Weight		
BMI		BMI		
Waist–hip ratio		Waist–hip ratio		
Chest, relaxed		Chest, relaxed		
Chest, expanded		Chest, expanded		
Waist		Waist		
Stomach		Stomach		
Hips		Hips		
Neck		Neck		
Shoulders		Shoulders		
Right upper arm, relaxed		Right upper arm, relaxed		
Right upper arm, flexed		Right upper arm, flexed		
Left upper arm, relaxed		Left upper arm, relaxed		
Left upper arm, flexed		Left upper arm, flexed		
Right forearm, relaxed		Right forearm, relaxed		
Right forearm, flexed		Right forearm, flexed		
Left forearm, relaxed		Left forearm, relaxed		
Left forearm, flexed		Left forearm, flexed		
Right upper thigh		Right upper thigh		
Right lower thigh		Right lower thigh		
Left upper thigh		Left upper thigh		
Left lower thigh		Left lower thigh		
Right calf		Right calf		
Left calf		Left calf		

Time how long it takes to run 1 mile/2km.	Current		Target	
Count how many push-ups you can do before you have to stop.	Current		Target	
Count how many sit-ups you can do before you have to stop.	Current		Target	
Count how many squats you can do before you have to stop.	Current		Target	
Sit with legs out straight. Place a ruler on the floor with the tip between your feet. Record how many inches/cm you stretch up to or beyond your feet.	Current distance [+/-]		Target distance [+/-]	
Time you can balance on one foot: right leg left leg	Current		Target	

Cardiovascular Fitness Test		Last Month	Target	Actual	Next Mth's Target
Resting heart rate					
Working heart rate:	after 3 minutes				
	after 6 minutes				
	after 9 minutes				
Recovery heart rate:	at course completion				
	1 minute after completion				
	2 minutes after completion				
	3 minutes after completion				
Completion time					

Current Personal Summary

Strength level 1–5 ☐

Endurance level 1–5 ☐

Satisfaction with fitness 1–5 ☐

Satisfaction with weight 1–5 ☐

Quality of diet 1–5 ☐

Energy level 1–5 ☐

Sleep quality 1–5 ☐

Stress level 1–5 ☐

Mood level 1–5 ☐

End-of-Year Personal Summary

Yearly Heart-Rate Graph

Record your average weekly resting and maximum heart rates and graph your progress throughout the year.

Diet and Exercise Notes